# SIRTFOOD DIET

The Ultimate Guide For Rapid Weight loss and a Healthy Life. Discovering the incredible benefits of sirtfood that allows you to burn fat like never before.

**G.S. Van Leeuwen**

# Disclaimer

The information contained in " SIRTFOOD DIET is meant to serve as a comprehensive collection of strategies that the author of this eBook has done research about. Summaries, strategies, tips and tricks are only recommendation by the author, and reading this eBook will not guarantee that one's results will exactly mirror the author's results. The author of the eBook has made all reasonable effort to provide current and accurate information for the readers of the eBook. The author and it's associates will not be held liable for any unintentional error or omissions that may be found. The material in the eBook may include information by third parties. Third party materials comprise of opinions expressed by their owners. As such, the author of the eBook does not assume responsibility or liability for any third party material or opinions. Whether because of the progression of the internet, or the unforeseen changes in company policy and editorial submission guidelines,  what is stated as fact at the time of this writing may become autdated or inapplicable later.

The eBook is copyright © 2020 with all rights reserved. It is illegal to redistribute , copy, or create derivative work from this eBook whole or in part. No parts of this report may be reproduced or retransmitted in any reproduced or retransmitted in any forms whatsoever without the writing expressed and signed permission from the author.

# Sommario

# Introduction

Let's start at the beginning. The Sirtfood diet came to the fore through Instagram - of course. It promises to lose up to 3 kilos a week without eliminating some things that it costs to strike down, chocolate or red wine.

After these first promises, it was also leaked that it is an exclusive diet that was designed for a group of celebrities in one of the most TOP gyms in London that some like Madonna or Daniel Craig go to. Their creators? Renowned Aidan Goggins and Glen Matten, both nutritionists.

## What Is Sirtfood?

The Sirtfood diet was developed by two renowned nutritionists working in a private gym in the UK. They advertise the diet as a revolutionary plan for losing weight and improving health, which can trigger changes in the body at the cellular level.

In general, the diet is based on studies of sirtuins, a group of seven proteins found in the body. They regulate various functions, including metabolism, inflammation, and longevity. Some natural plant compounds are able to increase the level of these proteins in the body. And the products containing them received the name "sirfoods" from the authors of the diet.

List of "20 best food" for the Sirtfood diet includes:

- Kale cabbage
- Red wine
- Strawberry
- Bow
- Soybean
- Parsley
- Olive oil
- Dark chocolate (minimum 85% cocoa)
- Japanese matcha green tea

- Buckwheat
- Turmeric
- Walnuts
- Arugula
- Pepper Flame
- Lovage
- Dates Salad chicory
- Blueberries Capers
- Coffee

The diet combines these so-called sweet foods and calorie restriction. Both one and the other, supposedly, can increase the level of sirtuins in the body. The creators of the diet claim that thanks to this, the Sirtfood diet will lead to rapid weight reduction while maintaining muscle mass and protecting against chronic diseases.

## How the Sirrfood Diet Works

Sirtfood diet consists of two phases, which last a total of three weeks. After that, you can partially continue the diet by including as many sirfoods as possible in regular dishes. Specific recipes for these two phases are contained in The Sirtfood Diet, written by the creators of the diet. To follow a diet, you have to buy it. However, there are already alternative recipe books and even recipes in the public domain. The bad news is that almost all of them are in various languages. If you do not know the language, you will have to ask someone to translate them.

There may also be a problem with finding all the ingredients necessary for a diet. Matcha and lovage Japanese powdered green tea are not the most popular and affordable products. The most important part of the diet is the juice, which will need to be made one to three times a day. To get this, you need a juicer and a kitchen scale, since the ingredients are measured strictly by weight.

Sirtfood Juice Recipe

- 75 g kale
- 30 grams of arugula
- 5 g parsley
- two sticks of celery
- 1 cm ginger

- Half green apple
- Half a lemon
- Half a teaspoon of matcha green tea powder

All ingredients except green tea and lemon are passed through a juicer and poured into a glass. Lemon juice is squeezed by hand. Then green tea powder is added, and everything is mixed.

### The first stage of the diet

The first stage lasts seven days and includes calorie restriction and a lot of juice. At this stage, weight loss starts - in a week, you should lose 3.2 kg. During the first three days of the first phase, calorie intake is limited to 1000 calories per day. You drink three glasses of juice a day, plus one meal. The recipe is selected only from the list allowed for the diet. For example, it can be scrambled eggs or shrimp with buckwheat noodles.

On days 4 through 7, calorie intake rises to 1,500. Now you need to drink two glasses of juice a day and eat two main dishes from the list.

### The second stage of the diet

The second stage lasts two weeks, in which you must continue to lose weight. There is no particular calorie limit for this phase. Instead, you eat three main meals a day and drink one glass of juice. Again, dishes are selected from recipes presented in the book or on special sites.

## After the diet,

The two phases of the diet can be repeated as often as required for further weight loss. In addition, it is recommended that you continue to add sirfood dishes to your diet even after returning to your normal diet. It is also advised that you continue to drink Sirtfood juice every day. Thus, the Sirtfood diet is more like a lifestyle change than a short-term diet.

## Is It Effective?

The authors of the diet make the most daring statements about this. The problem is that there is not enough evidence to support their words. There is no convincing evidence that the Sirtfood diet helps you lose weight more effectively than any other calorie-restricted diet.

Although many of the recommended foods are undoubtedly useful, there have not been any long-term studies in humans that can confirm that overall, such a diet provides tangible health benefits. The original Sirtfood Diet book presents the results of a pilot study conducted by the authors themselves, in which 39 volunteers from the fitness center participated. During the week, participants followed a diet and trained daily. Towards its end, they lost an average of 3.2 kg and retained or even gained muscle mass. But these results are unlikely to surprise anyone. Limiting food intake to 1000 calories a day while doing sports always leads to weight loss. The fact is that when the body is deprived of energy, it uses its reserves, in particular glycogen, in addition to burning fat and muscles. Each glycogen molecule binds 3-4 water molecules in the body. When the body uses glycogen, it also disposes of this water. As a result, we quickly lose weight, but not at the expense of fat. It has been proven that in the first week of extreme calorie restriction, only about one-third of weight loss occurs in fat, while the other two-thirds are water, muscle, and glycogen.

As for calorie intake increases, the body replenishes glycogen stores, and the weight returns. Unfortunately, this kind of calorie restriction can also lead to the fact that the body will reduce the metabolic rate, which will not contribute to further weight loss. That is, probably, the Sirtfood diet can really help to lose a few pounds right at the start, but they will return as soon as the diet is over.

As for the disease prevention promised by the authors, then three weeks is clearly not enough time to seriously affect health. On the other hand, adding sugar foods to your regular diet, in the long run, may well be a good idea. True, in this case, the diet itself can be skipped.

## How to Follow the Sirtfood Diet

This nutrition program can be divided into two phases: the so-called march throw (during which you lose excess weight) and fastening. The "march throw" is designed for a week, during which you lose about 3 - 3.5 kg. Having fixed the result, the "march-throw" is repeated - once a month, until the necessary results are obtained. After you gain the weight of your dreams, it is recommended to repeat the "march throw" once every three months.

**Get ready to drink plenty of green juice. It is prepared as follows:**

2 handfuls of curly cabbage mixed in a blender with a handful of arugula and a handful of parsley, grind into gruel. Add 150 g of celery, including leaves, half a green apple, half lemon juice and a teaspoon of matcha tea powder. Dilute the mixture with still water for a more comfortable drink. Drink this juice should be 1 to 2 hours before meals.

**Sirt Food Diet: The First Three Days**

The throw march begins. The first three days you need to drink 3 servings of green juice per day and eat one full meal of the recommended (see above) foods. Snacks are also acceptable, but your "limit" of calories is limited to 1000 calories per day.

## Sirtfood diet: the next four days

We continue to drink green juice (two servings a day) and allow ourselves two full meals with snacks. Calorie Limit: 1500.

Weight loss at this stage will be 3 - 3.5 kg. If you feel that you can last longer than four days, feel free to continue this diet for another week. The plumb in this case will be even greater.

## Sirtfood Diet: Securing Results

For the period of consolidation is not provided for any strict rules. "Just try to include as many "syrfoods "in your diet as possible in order to feel healthier, more energetic and improve the condition of your skin, as well as becoming even slimmer," says Aidan Goggins.

Keep drinking green juice (one serving a day). General recommendations: dinner should be no later than seven o'clock in the evening, exclude processed foods from the diet, reduce the amount of red meat to 500 g per week. Red wine is allowed and even encouraged, but you can drink it no more than 3 times a week.

This phase can last as long as you need. Many who have appreciated the benefits of sirtfood in their experience prefer to build their entire diet on the basis of sirtfoods.

Sirtfood Meal Plan and 3 Weeks Plan

## Losing Weight Like Adele: The Sense And Nonsense Of The Sirt Food Diet

Since singer Adele lost tens of kilos with it, the sirt food diet has been in the spotlight. What exactly is sirt food and what are the effects of this diet regime?

## Question 1: What is the sirt food diet?

Sirt stands for sirtuin. Foods that contain that substance would stimulate fat burning, improve muscle growth and be good for your health. Examples of sirt foods are cocoa, green tea, walnuts, coffee, turmeric and red onions. British creators Aidan Goggins and Glen Matten, both nutritionists, call the diet "the revolutionary health and weight loss plan." It takes place in two stages. The first week should be the strictest: then you limit yourself to a maximum of two low-calorie meals a day and you mainly drink juices from sirt foods.

This is followed by the maintenance phase: three healthy meals a day for two weeks, one green juice and a maximum of one sirt food snack. You don't eat anything after seven in the evening. After those three weeks, according to the authors, your body gets a fat-burning boost and you lose more than 3 kilos. After this you only have to add a lot of sirtfoods to your diet and possibly repeat the first stages.

## Question 2: What do sirtuins do?

"Sirtuins are body's own enzymes, proteins", says Ingeborg Brouwer, professor of nutrition for healthy living at VU University Amsterdam. "The letters 'sir' stands for silent information regulators.

These substances have an important function in our body. They play a role in the regulation of our dna and rna, the genetic material in our cells. They are important in the prevention of cell aging. When you fast, your body produces more sirtuins. This also happens with exercise. The theory is that eating sirt foods has the same effect as fasting and exercising. Among other things, it would increase your metabolism and stimulate fat burning. "

These proteins are indeed in the mentioned foods. But proteins from food are broken down when they are absorbed. They are unlikely to do the same in the body as our body's own enzymes. Whether they cause you to lose weight, I doubt. The sirttfood diet allows you to consume up to 1000 calories in the first three days. Then you lose weight anyway. "

## Question 3: Is following this diet heavy?

According to the proponents, it is a piece of cake. The group of foods also has an effect on your brain. The substances are said to regulate hunger via the taste center in your brain. Therefore, you would not feel hungry even in the strictest phase. Since you mimic the effect of exercise with the diet, you don't need to lose yourself in the gym. "The recommended foods fit in well with a healthy diet. You also don't eat too much of it quickly, " says professor Brouwer. Still, there are things to keep in mind. For example, the benefit of chocolate only applies to 85 percent dark chocolate. "Anyone who has ever eaten that knows that the taste is very bitter. The temptation to eat too much is small. "

The weight of the diet also depends on whether it suits you, says Brouwer, who conducts research on diet and depression, among other things. "Not eating after seven in the evening can be a good idea for many people because they consume less, but it has to fit into your life."

## Question 4: Are the effects scientifically proven?

Although the diet is 'clinically proven' according to the authors, no large-scale research has been done, Brouwer knows. "Studies with fruit flies and mice have shown that the substances mentioned have beneficial effects, but more research is needed to substantiate the authors' claims."

According to Brouwer, the choice of raw food and fresh products is consistent with the Mediterranean diet, which consists of many fresh vegetables and olive oil. "It has been proven that it contributes to a longer life expectancy and a better quality of life."

Brouwer suspects that the promised weight loss is mainly related to the limited calorie intake. "It's about healthy eating with few calories. In that respect, the diet is not revolutionary. "

## Question 5: What if you don't have to lose weight?

Not only superstars swear by the diet plan. Athletes also follow it, because of the beneficial health effects. According to creators Goggins and Matten, a lack of sirtuins in the body plays a role in many diseases, such as diabetes and Alzheimer's disease. Due to its positive effects on muscle building, it would also be good for the heart.

Brouwer: I don't see any major disadvantages. You eat healthy, unprocessed foods and because there are no restrictions on other foods, you do not run out of shortages quickly. Make sure that you do not lose weight with too little or one-sided food. Simply varied, not eating too much and healthy food works best."

Examples of sirtfoods - Dark chocolate (85% cocoa) - Kale - Red onion - Blueberries - Turmeric - Strawberries - Soy - Matcha green tea - Olive oil - Capers - Parsley - Citrus Fruit

- Apples - Red praise - Rocket - Walnuts - Buckwheat - Red Wine - Coffee (in moderation)

## Meal Planning

This nutrition program can be divided into two phases: the so-called march throw (during which you lose excess weight) and fastening. The "march throw" is designed for a week, during which you lose about 3 - 3.5 kg. Having fixed the result, the "march-throw" is repeated - once a month, until the necessary results are obtained. After you gain the weight of your dreams, it is recommended to repeat the "march throw" once every three months.

**Get ready to drink plenty of green juice. It is prepared as follows:**

2 handfuls of curly cabbage mixed in a blender with a handful of arugula and a handful of parsley, grind into gruel. Add 150 g of celery, including leaves, half a green apple, half lemon juice and a teaspoon of matcha tea powder. Dilute the mixture with still water for a more comfortable drink. Drink this juice should be 1 to 2 hours before meals.

**Sirt Food Diet: The First Three Days**

The throw march begins. The first three days you need to drink 3 servings of green juice per day and eat one full meal of the recommended (see above) foods. Snacks are also acceptable, but your "limit" of calories is limited to 1000 calories per day.

## Sirtfood diet: the next four days

We continue to drink green juice (two servings a day) and allow ourselves two full meals with snacks. Calorie Limit: 1500.

Weight loss at this stage will be 3 - 3.5 kg. If you feel that you can last longer than four days, feel free to continue this diet for another week. The plumb in this case will be even greater.

## Sirtfood Diet: Securing Results

For the period of consolidation is not provided for any strict rules. "Just try to include as many "syrfoods" in your diet as possible in order to feel healthier, more energetic and improve the condition of your skin, as well as becoming even slimmer," says Aidan Goggins.

Keep drinking green juice (one serving a day). General recommendations: dinner should be no later than seven o'clock in the evening, exclude processed foods from the diet, reduce the amount of red meat to 500 g per week. Red wine is allowed and even encouraged, but you can drink it no more than 3 times a week.

This phase can last as long as you need. Many who have appreciated the benefits of sirtfood in their experience prefer to build their entire diet on the basis of sirtfoods.

# The Sirrfood Diet Recipes

## 1. RABBIT WITH APPLES

Energy Value Per Portion

- Calorie Content: 685 Kcal
- Squirrels: 64.3 Gram
- Fats: 37,4 Gram
- Carbohydrates: 21.3 Gram

INGREDIENTS

- Rabbit legs - 4 pieces
- Garlic - 2 cloves
- An Apple - 4 pieces
- Thyme - 4 stems
- Olive oil - 50 ml
- Salt – taste

PREPARATION

1. Crush the cloves of garlic with a knife, add olive oil to them, add thyme and salt, mix all this and marinate the rabbit legs for about an hour.
2. Put the pickled rabbit in a deep form and put in the oven, preheated to 180 degrees, for forty minutes.

3. When this time is up, send the apples cut into large slices into the same form. Bake another fifteen minutes.
4. Serve rabbit legs with baked apples or boiled rice.

## 2. HUNGARIAN APPLE PIE

**ENERGY VALUE PER PORTION**

- Calorie Content: 785 Kcal
- Squirrels: 8.7 Gram
- Fats: 27 Gram
- Carbohydrates: 126.9 Gram

**INGREDIENTS**

- Wheat flour - 130 g
- Sugar - 150 g
- Semolina - 160 g
- Baking powder - 7 g
- Cinnamon - ½ teaspoon
- Butter - 120 g
- An Apple - 7 pieces

**PREPARATION**

1. Mix flour, semolina, sugar, baking powder and cinnamon in a separate bowl.
2. Wash apples, peel and seed boxes and rub on a coarse grater.
3. We bake the baking dish with baking paper or foil and generously grease with butter.
4. Pour a part of the dry mixture to the bottom of the mold - the layer should not be too thick, and even out. Then we spread the grated apples - with a layer of about the same thickness, level them. Alternating layers spread the whole dry mixture and apples, the last should be a dry layer. I got three dry and two apple layers. Grate the butter on top.
5. Preheat the oven to 180 degrees. Bake the cake for 40–45 minutes - the crust should become rosy.

ENERGY VALUE PER PORTION

- Calorie Content: 220 Kcal
- Squirrels: 4,5 Gram
- Fats: 7 Gram
- Carbohydrates: 34.1 Gram

## INGREDIENTS

- Yellow apples - 1 kg
- Wheat flour - 150 g
- Sugar - 120 g
- Milk - 100 ml
- Chicken egg - 3 pieces
- Lemon - 1 piece
- Baking powder - 1 teaspoon
- Salt – pinch
- Butter - 50 g
- Cinnamon – taste

## PREPARATION

1. Peel and finely chop apples into slices, pour over lemon juice so that they do not darken (sisters recommend the Golden variety).

2. Beat eggs with sugar, salt, zest; add flour with baking powder and milk. Beat everything until smooth.
3. Grease a baking sheet using butter and sprinkle with sugar (a little).
4. Mix 2/3 of the apples with the dough, and randomly put the remaining third on a baking sheet from above (preferably in a round shape 27–28 cm in size). Do not be alarmed - the dough seems very small, but there are a lot of apples. It kind of slightly envelops apples, and that's the point. In the oven, it rises.
5. Take solid butter and put in tiny pieces on apples, sprinkle on top with sugar and cinnamon to taste.
6. Preheat the oven to 180 degrees and bake for 35–40 minutes.
7. You can leave a few slices to put them nicely on top of the cake.

## 4. WULFS APPLE PIE

**ENERGY VALUE PER PORTION**

- Calorie Content: 676 Kcal
- Squirrels: 10,4 Gram
- Fats: 41 Gram

- Carbohydrates: 65,4 Gram

**INGREDIENTS**

- Puff pastry - 500 g
- Sour cream 20% - 400 g
- Honey - 100 g
- Chicken egg - 2 pieces
- An Apple - 5 items
- Butter - 50 g
- Cinnamon – taste

**PREPARATION**

1. Roll out the puff pastry; put it in a baking sheet. Fry the apples in butter until soft, add honey, cinnamon, mix and remove from heat.
2. Lightly beat the sour cream with two eggs and mix with apples. Put apples and sour cream on rolled dough; wrap the edges of the dough. Lubricate with the remaining beaten egg and place for thirty to forty minutes in the oven, heated to 200 degrees.

## 5. ALSATIAN APPLE PIE

**INGREDIENTS**

- Butter - 120 g
- Wheat flour - 180 g
- Salt - ⅓ teaspoon
- Egg yolk - 2 pieces
- Lingonberry - 50 g
- An Apple - 4 pieces
- Chicken egg - 2 pieces
- Sugar - 120 g
- Milk - 150 ml
- Lemon juice - 2 tablespoons

## PREPARATION

1. Prepare the dough. To do this, mix the butter with sugar, add 2 yolks, salt and flour.
2. Knead the dough. Form a lump and cool it for 10-15 minutes.
3. Mash the chilled dough in a baking dish greased with oil or lined with parchment baking paper. Pierce with a fork.
4. Bake for 15 minutes in the oven.
5. The filling is done as follows: peel the apples and cut into slices. To prevent apples from darkening, pour them with lemon juice.
6. Fry the apples in a small amount of oil until golden brown.

7. Put the apples in a rose and sprinkle with frozen lingonberries on top, although other berries, such as black currants, are also suitable.
8. For the sauce, mix 2 eggs, 4 tablespoons of sugar and milk.
9. Pour the pie mixture with the mixture.
10. Bake in the oven for 30 minutes.

## INGREDIENTS

- Wheat flour - 1 cup
- Sugar - 1 cup
- Semolina - 1 cup
- Butter - 50 g
- Soda - 1 teaspoon
- An Apple - 1,5 kg

## PREPARATION

1. Mix flour, sugar, semolina and soda.
2. Wash apples, peel and rub on a fine grater.
3. Lubricate the deep form with oil.
4. And the fun begins! We spread the resulting mixture in layers: 1 layer - a dry mixture, 2 layers - grated apples, etc. (I get about 3 apple layers and, accordingly, 4 from dry ingredients), the last layer should be from flour, sugar and semolina!
5. We equate everything, rub on top with frozen (!) Oil (sometimes use margarine for baking Pyshechka).
6. Put in the oven for about 1 hour at 150-200 degrees.

7. Check the readiness with a toothpick; it is necessary that the cake is not wet!
8. We get it, turn it into a dish and wait for it to cool completely.

## 7. PROVENCAL APPLE PIE WITH WALNUTS

**Energy Value Per Portion**

- Calorie Content: 310 Kcal
- Squirrels: 6.8 Gram
- Fats: 6.4 Gram
- Carbohydrates: 55 Gram

**INGREDIENTS**

- Egg white - 2 pieces
- Cane sugar - ½ cup
- Vanilla extract - 1 teaspoon
- Baking powder - 1 teaspoon
- Ground cinnamon - ½ teaspoon
- Wheat flour - ½ cup
- Walnuts - 35 g
- An Apple - 2 pieces

PREPARATION

1. Peel the apples, cut it into half and remove the core. Cut into small cubes.

2. Preheat the oven to 180 degrees. Butter a small baking pan or pan.
3. In a bowl, beat the whites, vanilla, sugar, baking powder and cinnamon. Then add flour, nuts and apples. Mix well.
4. Transfer the dough into the prepared form and bake for 30 minutes until cooked.

## 8. WARSAW APPLE PIE

## INGREDIENTS

- An Apple - 7 pieces
- Wheat flour - 1 cup
- Semolina - 1 cup
- Sugar - 1 cup
- Butter - 100 g
- Lemon - 1 piece
- Cinnamon – taste
- Orange zest – taste

## PREPARATION

1. To prepare the filling, wash the apples, peel and grate on a coarse grater. Pour the apples with lemon juice so that they do not darken. Sprinkle

apples with cinnamon, you can also add orange zest.

2.  Take a round baking dish and line it with baking paper. If you do not have paper, you can oil the mold. But keep in mind that the Warsaw pie is crumbly, so if you bake it without paper, then it will be difficult to get it out of shape. Combine the flour, semolina, sugar and baking powder and pour a third of the flour mixture into the bottom of the mold. After leveling, lay on top a third of the apples. Alternate layers of apples and dry mix. Lay slices of margarine or butter on the last layer.

3.  Bake the Warsaw pie in the oven, heated to 180-200 degrees, for 30-40 minutes (a crust should appear on the pie). Remove the cake from the oven, cool and transfer to a dish - and Warsaw apple pie can be served.

## Energy Value Per Portion

- Calorie Content: 488 Kcal
- Squirrels: 10.7 Gram
- Fats: 5.9 Gram
- Carbohydrates: 97.5 Gram

## INGREDIENTS

- Sugar - 1 cup
- Chicken egg - 3 pieces
- Wheat flour - 1 cup
- An Apple - 2 pieces
- Baking powder - ½ teaspoon

## PREPARATION

1. Break three eggs into a bowl, add sugar and beat with a mixer until white foam.
2. Then add flour and baking powder, and mix everything.
3. Cut the apples into slices, remove the core.
4. Grease a baking dish with butter, sprinkle with breadcrumbs and lay apples on the bottom. Pour dough and bake for about 40 minutes at medium temperature. The readiness of the pie can then be

checked with a toothpick or a match - the pie is ready when the dough does not stick to the toothpick when it is immersed deep into the pie.

## INGREDIENTS

- Cinnamon – pinch
- Cottage cheese - 500 g
- An Apple - 1 kg
- Baking powder - 1 teaspoon
- Margarine - 200 g
- Sugar - 1.5 cups
- Wheat flour - 2 cups
- Sour cream - 100 g
- Chicken egg - 4 pieces

## PREPARATION

1. For the test, grind 3 yolks (we carefully separate them with proteins) with 0.5 cups of sugar, then grind with softened (not melted) margarine (butter), then introduce the flour, baking powder, knead a rather thick dough with your hands, finally mix in roll sour cream into a bowl, cover and refrigerate for at least half an hour while the filling is being prepared and the oven is preheated

2. Rub the cottage cheese, mix with 1/3 cup sugar and 1 yolk (add the protein from the egg to the remaining three)

3. Peel the apples and seeds, cut into thin slices (until the dough is rolled out, it is better to sprinkle them with lemon juice or diluted citric acid so that they do not darken, but you can cut them already when the cake is ready to be planted in the oven).

4. Roll out the dough thin enough on a rather large baking sheet, making sides along the edges (so that the curd does not drip). We spread evenly the curd filling, beautifully lay the apple slices on it, and sprinkle with cinnamon. We put the oven preheated to 200 degrees for 30-40 minutes.

5. While the cake is baking, beat the whites with the remaining sugar in a thick foam.

6. Take out the slightly baked cake and lay the protein foam over the apples evenly, level it and put it in the hot oven again. When in a few minutes the squirrels grab a light brown crust - the cake is ready!!!

## 11. DORADO WITH CITRUS PESTO SAUCE

**INGREDIENTS**

- 2 servings
- 2 pcs Dorado (whole)
- 20 gr Basil

- 1.5 tbsp. l Pine nuts
- 1/4 pcs Lemon (juice and zest)
- 40 ml Olive oil (plus fish oil)
- 1 tbsp. l Parmesan (grated)
- Rosemary / thyme / garlic optional

## PREPARATION

1. To clean the fish, remove the gills and make deep cruciform incisions on each side. Season and grease with olive oil (I put it inside on a sprig of thyme and rosemary and a clove of garlic). Bake for 20-30 minutes inside the oven or cook on the barbecue.
2. Cook the pesto. To do this, punch basil in a blender (leave a few leaves for decoration), pine nuts, parmesan, lemon juice and lemon peel and olive oil fried in a dry pan. Add another clove of garlic.
3. Serve the fish with pesto sauce and garnish with basil leaves

## INGREDIENTS

- 1.5 kg Mandarin
- 5-6 pcs. Oranges
- 1 kg. Sugar
- 1 stick Cinnamon
- 2 tbsp. Pectin
- 2 tbsp. Sahara

## PREPARATION

1. Peel tangerines, oranges. I added 1/4 orange zest.
2. Pour sugar overnight. In the morning
3. Mix everything and put it to boil, add cinnamon during the cooking process.
4. After about 30 minutes of cooking, mix the pectin with sugar and pour into the jam
5. Mix well and boil for another 1 minute.
6. Remove from heat, cool, pour into banks.

## 13.CITRUS CURD CASSEROLE

## INGREDIENTS

- 500 grams cottage cheese
- 100g natural yogurt
- 2 pcs the eggs
- 100g rice flour
- Orange zest
- 10 grams vanilla or vanilla sugar
- Taste Sugar

## PREPARATION

1. Beat cottage cheese, yogurt and eggs with a blender. Grate the orange peel on a fine grater. Add the zest to the resulting mixture and mix.
2. Add flour, sugar and vanilla to the finished mixture. Preheat the oven to 180 *. Bake until cooked for 30-40 minutes.

## 14.BLUEBERRY CITRUS SMOOTHIE

## INGREDIENTS

- Banana - 2 pcs.
- Orange juice - 2 tbsp.
- Sugar demerara from the mistral - 1 tablespoon
- Blueberries - 2/3 tbsp.
- Ginger - a pinch

## PREPARATION

1. Break a banana into pieces.
2. Add blueberries.
3. Add orange juice and a pinch of ginger to the blender bowl.
4. Beat everything in a blender bowl.
5. Pour into glasses, garnish with blueberries or a slice of orange.

## 15.COCKTAIL OF THREE TYPES OF CITRUS WITH MAPLE SYRUP

## INGREDIENTS

- Orange juice - 30 ml.
- Grapefruit juice - 30 ml.
- Lemon juice - 15 ml.
- Maple syrup - 15 ml.
- Ice - 5 cubes

- Highly carbonated mineral water - 50 ml.
- 

## PREPARATION

1. Squeeze juice from orange, grapefruit, lemon.
2. Measure the required amount and pour into a shaker.
3. Send there the maple syrup and 5 ice cubes. Beat.
4. Pour the contents of the shaker right into a glass, add mineral water and 2 ice cubes and serve!

## 16.QUINOA, SHRIMP AND CITRUS SALAD

## INGREDIENTS

- Salad leaves - 50-70 gr.
- Mistral Quinoa - 1 Cup
- Peeled shrimps (large) - 100 gr.
- Citrus mix (filet grape + sweet) - 150 gr.
- Parmesan (chopped) - 50 gr.
- Salt
- Pepper
- Sweet red pepper
- Vegetable oil for frying

- Olive oil

## PREPARATION

1. Make KINOA groats according to the directions on the packaging.
2. Slightly fry the shrimps in vegetable oil, salt a little, sprinkle with sweet red pepper.

Prepare salad dressing:

3. Mix in equal amounts (3-4 tablespoons) olive oil and citrus juice.
4. Salt, pepper, to taste.
5. Dress the resulting quinoa cereal with the resulting sauce.
6. Add the parmesan and lettuce leaves.
7. Put the mixture in a salad bowl with shrimp and citrus slices.

### 17.CITRUS MIX PUDDING

## INGREDIENTS

- Citruses - 3 pcs. (Sweet + grape + orange)
- Eggs - 2 pcs. (s)
- Corn starch - 2 tbsp.
- Cane sugar

- Unrefined demerara from the mistral - 3 tbsp. +4 tsp
- Baked milk - 350 ml.
- Wheat bread - 150-170 g.

## PREPARATION

1. Prepare citrus fruits: wash the fruits, cut the peel with a sharp knife, cut the fillet between the separation membranes, cut the citrus pulp into pieces.
2. Beat eggs with 3 tbsp. of cane sugar, add starch, mix, stir constantly, and pour in cold milk.
3. Prepare pudding molds (4 200 ml refractory cups.)
4. Turn on the oven 180 degrees. Put the water to heat up (~ 1.5 liters)
5. Bread (yesterday's and further ... baking) cut into a dice, or cut into the shape of a glass (you need two "circles" per glass).
6. Place the bread disks in the milk mixture; let them "get wet" well.
7. At the bottom of the glass, put the bread circle, then 1 tbsp. of citrus pulp, pour 2 tbsp. milk mixture (mix, as starch has the ability to "settle"), then repeat - bread + citruses + pour the remaining milk. Top with a teaspoon of cane sugar in each glass.

8. Place glasses with puddings in a baking dish; pour hot water into the pan between the glasses (half the pan).
9. Cook the puddings for about 30 minutes. During cooking, the top of the pudding rises, the sugar is caramelized.

Serve puddings in any form. Or immediately after cooking, or let them cool and put in the refrigerator.

# 18.CARROT SALAD WITH CITRUS MARINADE WITH CHANAH CHEESE

## INGREDIENTS

- Carrots - 3 pcs.
- Orange - 1 pc.
- Lime - 1 pc.
- Sugar - 3 tablespoons
- Chanakh cheese - 100 g
- Cilantro - 3 branches
- Chili pepper - 1/4 pc.
- Pine nuts - a handful
- Vegetable oil for deep fat - 1
- Pea seedlings for decoration
- Salt, freshly ground pepper

## PREPARATION

1. Wash the carrots, chop with thin cubes;
2. Pour vegetable oil to the bowl of the multicooker no more than up to the "1" mark, that is, no more than 1 liter, close the lid and turn on the FRYTUR program, short mode;
3. When the oil is heated to the temperature necessary for frying, the countdown will begin,

open the lid, insert the basket, put the carrots in it, and fry with the lid open;

4. Cooking hot marinade. Squeeze the orange juice and remove the zest from it, combine in a small saucepan the juice and orange zest, half lime juice with 3 tbsp. sugar, add finely chopped chili, freed from seeds. Boil the syrup;

5. Carrots removed from the deep fryer, first spread on paper napkins to get rid of excess oil, then transfer to a bowl, fill with marinade and leave to stand for 10-15 minutes. Add cilantro leaves to the carrots;

6. Cheese chanah (can be replaced with feta or feta cheese) cut into small cubes;

7. Put carrots in a marinade with cilantro on a dish, slices of cheese, sprinkle with a handful of pine nuts, slightly fried in a dry pan, add salt to taste, garnish with pea seedlings. Season with freshly ground black pepper.

## 19. ORANGE CITRUS AND PERSIMMON SALAD

**INGREDIENTS**

- 1 grapefruit
- 1 orange

- 1 persimmon
- 2 tbsp. l acidophilus
- 1 tbsp. l balsamic sauce
- A pinch of orange pepper

## PREPARATION

1. With peeling grapefruit and orange.
2. Cut segments out of grapefruit.
3. Cut the orange into thin slices.
4. Cut persimmons into eights.
5. Put orange slices on a beautiful plate, then grapefruit segments and in the center of the persimmon wedges.
6. Sprinkle the whole composition with a pinch of orange pepper.
7. For the sauce, mix acidophilus and balsamic sauce.
8. Then you can pour fruit sauce, or you can just dip fruit slices in the sauce and enjoy.
9. If desired, you can pour fruit with honey or sprinkle with brown sugar.

# 20.MANNIK COTTAGE CHEESE "STRAWBERRIES WITH CREAM"

## INGREDIENTS

- Fat cottage cheese-800 gr.
- Semolina-5 tbsp.
- Eggs - 3-4 pcs.
- Salt-1/2 tsp
- Sugar 1/2 tbsp. (adjust to your liking)
- Vanilla
- Dried fruits (raisins or whatever you like. a citrus flavor, candied pamello)

For cream and filling:

- Fresh strawberries_200-300 gr.
- Fat cream (sour cream) -3-4 tablespoons
- Sugar.

## PREPARATION

1. Wipe the cottage cheese through a fine sieve.
2. Blatter the eggs with sugar, salt and vanilla, add the egg mixture to the curd, put the semolina, sliced candied fruit, mix and put into the mold, pregreased it with vegetable oil and sprinkled with cereal.

3. Cut the strawberries into plates; lay them tightly on the curd dough.

4. Separately, prepare the cream, whip the sour cream or cream with sugar and apply the cream on the strawberries.

5. Bake the manna until cooked, but do not overdo it in the oven.

## 21.PUMPKIN CITRUS DESSERT

## INGREDIENTS

- Pumpkin - 300 g
- Apple - 1 pc
- Orange - 2 pcs
- Honey - 1 tbsp.
- Cinnamon
- Vanillin

## PREPARATION

1. Dice Pumpkin
2. Peel the apple and also cut into cubes
3. Remove the zest from the oranges and squeeze the juice
4. Put pumpkin, apple, and zest in a saucepan, pour orange juice, add honey, cinnamon and vanillin to taste.

5. Put on fire and simmer under the lid for about 7-10 minutes.
6. Then turn it off and leave to cool.
7. When it cools down, mashed with a blender, put in a bowl and put in the refrigerator.
8. Let it brew (it took me a whole night), garnish with nuts, cream, or, as I had, a spoon of muesli.

## 22."LEMONADE" FROM.... CUCUMBERS

### INGREDIENTS

- 2 medium cucumbers
- 2 tbsp. lemon juice (can be replaced with any citrus)
- 2 tbsp. honey (can be replaced with sugar, but honey is healthier)
- 100-150 gr. water (boiled, non-carbonated, sparkling, purified, etc.)

### PREPARATION

1. Peel the cucumbers as thin as possible, cut into small rings.
2. Put cucumbers, lemon juice, honey and water in a blender and beat for five minutes until airy.

3. You can add ice to the heat. Chill out!

## 23.PINEAPPLE - CITRUS SORBET WITH LIQUOR

**INGREDIENTS**

- Pineapple - 1 pc. Weighing approximately 600 gr.
- Brown sugar - 40 gr.
- Lemon - 1 pc.
- Orange - 1 pc.
- Egg whites - 3 pcs.
- Water - 2 tbsp.
- Liqueur "maraschino" or any other - 10 ml.

**PREPARATION**

1. Pineapple peels and cut lengthwise into 4 parts. Remove the hard middle.
2. Cut into small pieces and grind in a blender until the consistency of mashed potatoes.
3. Wash the lemon and orange and remove only the top layer of the skin, cut into thin strips. Set aside.
4. Squeeze juice out of lemon and orange.
5. Mix water with sugar and heat over medium heat until the sugar is completely dissolved.
6. Add the citrus juice and boil for another 5 minutes, so that the liquid evaporates a little. Let it cool slightly.

7. Mix the resulting syrup with mashed potatoes, add liquor, and mix thoroughly.
8. Close the container with a lid or cling film and place in the freezer for 2 hours.
9. Remove and mix well until cream.
10. Cover and put in the freezer again for 1 hour.
11. Beat the squirrels in stable foam; gradually mix into a chilled mass.
12. Return to the freezer.
13. For 1 hour before use, get it; let it thaw a little, in order to get the consistency of melted ice cream.
14. Put in portioned bowls, garnish with strips of citrus or at your own discretion.

## 24. MULLED WINE

**Energy Value Per Portion**

- Calorie Content: 290 Kcal
- Squirrels: 0.9 Gram
- Fats: 0.4 Gram
- Carbohydrates: 43 Gram

**Ingredients**

- Sugar - 200 g
- An Apple - 2 pieces

- Oranges - 1 piece
- Cinnamon – pinch
- Nutmeg – pinch
- Clove - 1 piece
- Dry red wine - 1 liter

PREPARATION

1. Bring a mixture of wine, sugar, diced apples, sliced oranges and spices to a boil, remove from heat, and leave for 10 minutes. Then strain and pour into glasses.

## 25.CHRISTMAS MULLED WINE

**INGREDIENTS**

- Dry red wine - ¾ l
- Water - ¾ l
- An Apple - 2 pieces
- Oranges - 2 pieces
- Honey - 200 g
- Cinnamon – taste
- Clove – taste
- Anise (star anise) – taste
- Cardamom – taste

- Nutmeg – taste
- Ginger – taste
- Karkade - 1 tablespoon
- Black tea - 1 tablespoon

## PREPARATION

1. Pour water inside a pan and bring to a boil.
2. Pour tea and spices. Use must not be ground spices; otherwise the mulled wine will turn cloudy.
3. Pour wine, add chopped fruits and honey.
4. Without taking it to a boil, remove from heat.
5. Serve hot with gingerbread.

## INGREDIENTS

- Grape juice - 3 cups
- Water - ½ cup
- Orange zest - 2 tablespoons
- Lemon zest - 2 tablespoons
- An Apple - ½ pieces
- Raisins - 2 tablespoons
- Cinnamon - 1 teaspoon
- Clove - ½ teaspoon
- Cardamom – pinch
- Ginger - 1 g

## PREPARATION

1. Pour grape juice into the pan, add water and fill in all the other ingredients.

2. Put the pan on low heat, not boiling.

3. Allow the mulled wine to brew for 5 minutes under the lid and pour it into the glasses.

## 27.MULLED WINE WITH COFFEE AND COGNAC

**Energy Value Per Portion**

- Calorie Content: 245 Kcal
- Squirrels: 0.3 Gram
- Fats: 0 Gram
- Carbohydrates: 25,4 Gram

**Ingredients**

- Dry red wine - 750 ml
- Espresso - 1.5 cups
- Cognac - ¾ cup
- Sugar - 150 g

**PREPARATION**

1. Mix wine, coffee (espresso or just strong without thickening), brandy or brandy, sugar and put on moderate heat.

2. Stir until the sugar till it's dissolved, bring the mixture to a boil and immediately remove from heat.

3. Serve hot in mugs or refractory glasses.

## 28.FRUIT MULLED WINE

**Energy Value Per Portion**

- Calorie Content: 1297 Kcal
- Squirrels: 1.3 Gram
- Fats: 0.5 Gram
- Carbohydrates: 148.9 Gram

## Ingredients

- Wine in bags - 10
- Oranges - 1 kg
- An Apple - 1 kg
- Ground cinnamon – taste
- Ground cloves – taste
- Lemon2 pieces
- Honey – taste

## PREPARATION

1. Cut the fruit into slices; place all the ingredients in a saucepan.
2. Bring to a boil, crush the fruit a little, remove from heat and let it brew.

## 29.CHRISTMAS MULLED WINE WITH WHITE WINE AND ORANGES

## Energy Value Per Portion

- Calorie Content: 164 Kcal
- Squirrels: 0.5 Gram

- Fats: 0.2 Gram
- Carbohydrates: 20.6 Gram

## Ingredients

- Dry white wine - 750 ml
- Sugar - 100 g
- Water - ½ cup
- Cinnamon sticks - 1 piece
- Clove - 3 pieces
- Oranges - 1 piece

## Preparation

1. In a small saucepan, mix water with spices and sugar, add slices of orange and put on moderate heat.

2. While stirring it, bring the mixture to a boil and strain.

3. Mix the wine with the cooked broth and heat over moderate heat, not bringing to a boil.

3. Serve hot in refractory glass mugs.

### 30.WINTER MULLED WINE

## INGREDIENT

- Water - 1.5 cups
- Dry red wine - 1.5 cups

- Cinnamon sticks - 2 pieces
- Clove - 3 pieces
- Grated lemon zest – pinch
- Oranges - 1 piece
- Honey - 6 tablespoons
- Sugar - 2 tablespoons
- Anise (star anise) - 3 pieces
- Ground ginger - on the tip of a knife
- Black tea – taste

## PREPARATION

1. Pour water into a pot and bring to a boil.

2. Throw tea and spices.

3. Pour the wine and toss the sliced orange.

4. Add sugar and honey.

5. Cook for 6 minutes without boiling.

## 31.BUCKWHEAT MEATBALLS WITH MUSHROOMS

## INGREDIENTS

- Buckwheat groats - 200 g raw
- Potato - 2 pcs. (large)

- Champignons - 500 g
- Onions - 2 pcs.
- Dill - 20 g
- Vegetable oil - 2 tbsp.
- Ground black pepper and salt - to taste
- Flour for breading - 3-4 tbsp.

## PREPARATION

1. Cooking time depends on the preliminary preparation of the ingredients. If you boil potatoes and buckwheat in advance, then it will take you very little time to cook the cutlets themselves. We will sort and buckwheat. Boil buckwheat at the rate of 1 cup buckwheat in 2 cups of water, pour buckwheat with the boiling water, and add a pinch of salt. We prepare friable porridge, for this we simmer it over medium heat for 15-20 minutes after the water has boiled again. We need all the liquid to evaporate and the cereal to boil.
2. Boil the potatoes in their skins until ready in boiling water for 15-25 minutes. Cooking time depends on size and variety of potatoes. Check the potatoes for readiness with a fork or knife. The knife should easily enter the potato. Cool the finished potatoes, then peel and rub on a medium grater.
3. Onion cut into small cubes.

4. Pour the vegetable oil into the pan, heat it and fry the onions for 7 minutes, until tender, stirring occasionally.
5. Cut the mushrooms into a very small cube.
6. Add mushrooms to the onion, salt and pepper vegetables to taste. Cook the vegetables for another 10 minutes.
7. Now put in a bowl all the ingredients for our lean cutlets: boiled buckwheat, grated potatoes, fried mushrooms with onions, chopped dill. You can add seasoning for vegetables.
8. We shift the minced meat into a blender and punch it well until smooth.
9. We form cutlets of any shape from the resulting stuffing. Bone cutlets either in flour or in breadcrumbs. You can fry lean buckwheat cutlets with mushrooms in a pan with the addition of oil. Cook them in deep fat at 180 degrees 5 minutes. We put ready cutlets on a paper towel to get rid of excess oil.

## INGREDIENTS

- Chilled Chicken
- Boiled buckwheat - 200 g
- Onion - 1 head
- Garlic - 3 cloves
- Chicken Egg - 1 pc.
- Salt to taste
- Sunflower oil - for frying
- Bread to taste

## PREPARATION

1. Chicken breast and fillet cut from chicken legs are suitable for minced meat. We do not use skin. Twist the breast and fillet in a meat grinder.
2. Twist boiled buckwheat in chicken minced meat.
3. Onions and garlic. Let's break the chicken egg. Add salt.
4. Stir the minced meat into a homogeneous cutlet mass.
5. We form balls of the same size with wet hands. Roll the balls in breading, squeeze gently into the patty. We send the cutlets to a preheated pan. First, pour the sunflower oil into the pan.

6. Fry chicken cutlets with buckwheat on both sides over medium heat. Then close up the pan with a lid and switch to a slow fire. Bring our cutlets to readiness under the lid for 30 minutes.

## 33.BUCKWHEAT DIET CUTLETS

**INGREDIENTS**

- Buckwheat groats - 200 g
- Chicken Egg - 1 pc.
- Onion - 1 head
- Salt to taste
- Vegetable oil - for frying
- Breadcrumbs - to taste
- Fresh greens - to serve

**PREPARATION**

1. Boil buckwheat until fully cooked. In the process of cooking, buckwheat needs to be slightly salted. Buckwheat is cooked for 15-20 minutes, depending on the quality of the cereal. To make buckwheat friable, pour two fingers up on the water. Put the cooled boiled groats in a bowl. If you still have buckwheat porridge from breakfast, then blind the cutlets from it.

2. Onions cut into cubes. Add to buckwheat. Let's break the chicken egg.
3. A little salt does not hurt.
4. Using a submersible blender, mix everything into the buckwheat.
5. Add the breadcrumbs. Stir the minced meat with a spoon, add crackers in small portions until the stuffing becomes thick, with wet hands we will form buckwheat cutlets.
6. Preheat the pan. Add vegetable oil. Lightly brown the patties on one side.
7. Turnover and lightly brown on the other side. Then turn down the heat to a minimum. We put out the buckwheat cutlets under the lid for another 10 minutes. If necessary, add a third of a glass of water to the pan. Buckwheat diet cutlets are ready! Fast, cheap and cheerful.

## 34.BUCKWHEAT CUTLETS

**INGREDIENTS**

- Buckwheat (cooked) - 680 g
- Bouillon cube - 1 pc. (10 g);
- Onions - 0.5 pcs.

- Chicken Egg - 1 pc.
- Garlic - 2 cloves
- Breadcrumbs - 6 tbsp.
- Vegetable oil for frying - how much is needed

## PREPARATION

1. Cook in advance loose buckwheat porridge, let it cool. Also prepare bouillon cube, onion, egg, garlic, breadcrumbs, and vegetable oil. In crumbly buckwheat porridge, cooked in not too salty water, crumble the bouillon cube.
2. Break the egg in buckwheat, add the onion and garlic (large cubes).
3. In a blender or in a food processor, beat the buckwheat with the rest of the ingredients. All this should turn into a mass, reminiscent of both consistency and appearance of minced meat.
4. Blind cutlets from buckwheat mincemeat (15 pieces) and bread them in breadcrumbs.
5. Fry the buckwheat cutlets in vegetable oil until crusted. Since meatballs are not made from minced meat, they do not need to be fried for a long time or stewed later.

## INGREDIENTS

- Buckwheat groats - 1 cup
- Cottage cheese - 200-250 g
- Greens – optional
- Salt to taste
- Wheat flour - 1-2 tbsp.
- Spices to taste
- Oil - for frying
- Flour - for breading

## PREPARATION

1. Prepare buckwheat, cottage cheese, spices and flour.
2. Cook ordinary buckwheat from buckwheat (do not forget to salt it, but you cannot add oil).
3. Add cottage cheese, spices (you can take black pepper, curry, paprika, asafoetida ...), salt and any greens (fresh or dried), if any. Mash all ingredients thoroughly with your hands to get the most homogeneous mass. Add the flour a little to make the mincemeat begin to form well.
4. Form small cutlets, bread them in flour.
5. Fry in vegetable oil on both sides.

6. Serve hot cutlets of buckwheat and cottage cheese.

## 36.MEATBALLS WITH BUCKWHEAT IN A SLOW COOKER

**INGREDIENTS**

- Minced meat - 250 g
- Buckwheat - 1/2 cup
- Chicken Egg - 1 pc.
- Onions - 1-2 pcs.
- Carrots - 1 pc.
- Flour - 1 tbsp.
- Sour cream - 2 tablespoons
- Vegetable oil - 1 tbsp.
- Salt, pepper - to taste

**PREPARATION**

1. Boil buckwheat in advance until half cooked. Finely chop the onion or mince it with minced meat. In the bowl, put the minced meat, buckwheat, onion, add the egg. Salt and pepper to taste.

2. We mix the ingredients, let the minced meat "rest" for several minutes. We form meatballs weighing approximately 40-50 g.
3. In vegetable oil, fry meatballs with buckwheat in a slow cooker on both sides for 10 minutes in the "Frying" mode. Gently turn the meatballs with a plastic or wooden spoon.
4. Put the meatballs on a plate for now, cover with a bowl. We will prepare the sauce.
5. While the meatballs are fried, grate the carrots on a coarse grater, chop the onion finely. Let's send the vegetables to the slow cooker - to the oil remaining from frying. In the "Frying" mode, we spice the vegetables for 10 minutes, stirring.
6. Add flour, mix quickly. Add sour cream to the vegetables and pour water. If you like thick gravy - pour 2 cups of water, if more liquid - 3 cups. You can slightly salt and add spices. Now put the meatballs in the sauce. It is not necessary that they be completely covered with sauce.
7. Put the "Extinguishing" program for 20 minutes. And now our magnificent dish is ready! Delicate meatballs with buckwheat in sour cream sauce served with your favorite side dish or with fresh vegetables.

## INGREDIENTS

- Buckwheat - 150 g
- Water - 300 ml
- Onions - 150 g
- Carrots - 150 g
- Sunflower oil - 50 g
- Dill - 0.5 tsp
- Dried basil - 0.5 tsp
- Salt to taste
- Ground black pepper - to taste
- Ground caraway seeds - a pinch
- Breadcrumbs - 30 g

## PREPARATION

1. Boil buckwheat until cooked, without salt.
2. In sunflower oil, fry chopped onions and grated carrots until soft.
3. In a bowl of a food processor, simply place boiled buckwheat and fried vegetables. Grind to a puree state. You can grind several times in a meat grinder.

4. Add dried herbs, caraway seeds, salt, and pepper. Mix well. A viscous mass will be obtained from which it is easy to form cutlets.
5. Form cutlets of any size and breadcrumbs.
6. Heat oil in a pan. Sauté the lean buckwheat cutlets over medium heat until rosy. Since they are very fragile, carefully flip them to the other side.
7. Lay on a paper towel. Buckwheat meatballs are ready. Serve immediately

## 38.MEATBALLS WITH BUCKWHEAT AND MINCED MEAT

**INGREDIENTS**

- Buckwheat groats - 120 g
- Minced meat - 300 g
- Egg - 1 pc.
- Onions - 40 g
- Sour cream - 2 tablespoons
- Tomato paste - 1 tbsp.
- Sunflower oil - 40 ml
- Wheat flour - 1 tbsp.
- Salt to taste

**PREPARATION**

1. Boil buckwheat
2. Add minced meat, chopped onions and egg to buckwheat, salt, knead until smooth. Form small meatballs - the size may be what you are used to, make a little more than a walnut. Bread them in flour.
3. In warmed sunflower oil, fry meatballs with buckwheat and minced meat from all sides.
4. Flip to the other side. The sauce can be made right away, or can be prepared separately.
5. Dry the flour inside a dry frying pan until light pink and a nutty flavor appears. Cool slightly and dilute with water.
6. Dry the flour inside a dry frying pan until light pink and a nutty flavor appears. Cool slightly and dilute with water.
7. Stew meatballs in the resulting sauce.

## 39.BUCKWHEAT AND MINCED MEATBALLS

**INGREDIENTS**

- Minced meat - 500 g
- Boiled buckwheat - 200 g
- Onion - 1 pc.

- Garlic - 1 clove
- Chicken Egg - 1 pc.
- Flour - 3 tbsp.
- Vegetable oil - 3 tbsp.
- Salt, pepper - to taste

## PREPARATION

1. To prepare buckwheat cutlets with minced meat, we will prepare the products according to the list. Minced meat is better to use pork and beef. Buckwheat is better to pre-boil at the rate of 1 cup of cereal in 2.5 cups of water + salt. Cool the finished buckwheat.
2. Put the minced meat and buckwheat in a bowl.
3. Add the grated onion and let the garlic pass through the press.
4. Add the chicken egg, salt and pepper to the minced meat.
5. Mix the ingredients of the minced meat well.
6. From the minced meat we form cutlets of your usual shape.
7. Bread cutlets in flour.
8. Pour vegetable oil inside the pan and heat it. Fry the patties on one side for 4-5 minutes, then turn and fry the second side for 4-5 minutes. After that,

add 2-3 tbsp. water and then cover the pan with a lid. We put out the patties for another 10 minutes.

9. Cutlets with buckwheat and minced meat are ready!

# 40.VEGETARIAN CUTLETS WITH BUCKWHEAT AND POTATOES

## INGREDIENTS

- Buckwheat groats - 1 cup
- Potato - 500 g
- Flour - 4 tbsp.
- Spices to taste
- Salt to taste
- Vegetable oil - 3 tbsp.

## PREPARATION

1. Buckwheat should be washed, pour clean water and leave for 2-3 hours. The longer the buckwheat will stand, the more it will be in volume, up to a certain point, of course, but it must be soaked for at least an hour.
2. Now buckwheat can be chopped with a blender, but can be left as is. Add peeled grated peeled potatoes to the swollen buckwheat.
3. Stir, add salt and spices to taste
4. Stir; gradually add flour, stirring each time.
5. As soon as the mass begins to "sculpt" well, form cutlets. Bread them in flour.

6. Fry vegetarian cutlets with buckwheat and potatoes on both sides in a sufficient amount of oil (cutlets do not take oil in the same way as eggplants, but still). Fold the finished patties back into the pan, add some water and steam under the lid for a few more minutes.

## 41.EGGPLANT WITH WALNUT AND GARLIC

**INGREDIENTS**

- Eggplant - 2 pcs.
- Walnuts - 0.5 cups
- Garlic - 1-2 cloves
- Dill - 0.25 beams
- Parsley - 0.25 bunches
- Salt to taste
- Sunflower oil - for frying

**PREPARATION**

1. In eggplant, cut the tails and cut into slices 3-4 mm thick. Fold the eggplant in a bowl, salt and leave for 30 minutes, then pat it dry with napkins.
2. Heat sunflower oil inside a pan and fry the eggplant on both sides.
3. Then lay the eggplants on paper towels to remove excess oil.

4. Cook the filling. Put peeled walnuts, chopped garlic and herbs in a blender bowl. Garlic should be taken to taste, given the size of the cloves. As greens, Do dill and parsley; you can take cilantro if you like.
5. Grind the filling with the "metal knife" nozzle, then salt a little.
6. Put the fried eggplant strips on a plate, 1-2 tsp on the edge of the strip. Nut-garlic filling. Twist the eggplant into rolls.
7. Put eggplant rolls with walnuts and garlic on a plate, decorate with herbs. You can serve a snack to the table.

## 42.RED BEAN LOBIO

**INGREDIENTS**

- Red beans - 1-1.5 cups
- Walnuts - 0.5 cups
- Onion - 1 head
- Garlic - 1 clove
- Tomato juice - 0.5-1 cup
- Vegetable oil - 1-2 tbsp.
- Apple cider vinegar - 1 teaspoon
- Fresh (or dry greens) - to taste
- Ground peppers - to taste
- Hot pepper - 1 pod

- Salt - 1 pinch.

## PREPARATION

1. Beans must be soaked for a long time, for example, at night or for 5-8 hours.
2. Then fill with fresh water and cook until soft for about 1 hour. For the dish you will need beans without the resulting broth from cooking, although sometimes a little bean broth is added.
3. Chop walnuts and garlic.
4. Chop off the onion and fry a little in vegetable oil, and then add the prepared beans, tomato juice, walnuts and garlic to it.
5. Stir, add the hot pepper pod on top and simmer over low heat for 10-15 minutes.
6. At the very end of cooking, add greens: fresh and / or dry.

## 43.GEORGIAN EGGPLANT WITH NUTS

## INGREDIENTS

- Eggplant - 500 g
- Walnuts - 100 g
- Vinegar - 1/2 tsp

- Suneli hops to taste
- Garlic - 2 cloves
- Parsley - 20 g
- Cilantro - 20 g
- Salt to taste
- Ground black pepper - 1 pinch

## PREPARATION

1. Eggplant for this dish is better to take authentic, but not old. Cut them into strips 2 mm thick. Sprinkle eggplant with coarse salt. Leave them in salt for 10-15 minutes. During this time, eggplant will give their bitterness. After that, wash them under running water; dry them with paper towels to get rid of moisture.

2. Prepare a dietary version of the dish, fry eggplant; it will be in a dry grill pan. Firstly, the eggplant is juicy, and secondly, in the process of frying, a beautiful pattern on the eggplant strips is obtained, which will give the dish a beautiful appearance. Fry eggplant on both sides for 3-4 minutes. You can fry eggplant in vegetable oil in a pan, and on charcoal, and on a wire rack.

3. Prepare a nut filling. In a blender bowl, lay out walnuts, cilantro and parsley leaves, and cloves of

garlic, suneli hop and water. Punch everything in a blender to a puree state.

4. In the finished walnut puree, add wine vinegar, salt and black pepper.
5. Prepare the fried eggplant and nut filling and proceed to roll the rolls.
6. Spread a teaspoon of nut filling from the wide edge of the strip and gently twist the eggplant into a roll. Do this with all strips of eggplant.

**INGREDIENTS**

Dough:

- Flour - 460-500 g
- Butter - 200 g
- Sour cream - 200 g
- Salt - 0.3 tsp
- Vanillin - a pinch

Filling:

- Walnuts - 1.5 cups
- Sugar - 1 cup
- Honey - 2-3 tbsp.
- Egg - for lubrication
- Powdered sugar - for sprinkling
- Glass - 250 ml

**PREPARATION**

1. Sift flour and mix with vanilla and salt. Chop the butter and grind it with your hands with flour until fine crumbs are obtained.
2. In the center, make an hole and add sour cream.
3. Mix the dough with a spoon. Get friable mass, as in the photo. Then, with your hands, collect the

dough in a single lump and mix lightly so as not to delay the process.

4. Place the dough in a film and put in the refrigerator while preparing the filling.

5. Slightly fry the walnuts in a dry pan and grind in a blender until fine crumbs. It is undesirable to grind nuts until a smooth paste.

## 45.LUXURIOUS COOKIES

**INGREDIENTS**

- Chicken egg (protein) - 1 pc.
- Powdered Sugar - 50 g
- Walnuts - 50 g
- Coconut Chips - 50 g
- Chocolate - 50 g
- Prunes - 50 g

**PREPARATION**

1. Beat the egg white with powdered sugar into a white lush mass.

2. Add coconut and chopped chocolate.
3. Also chop coarsely nuts and chop prunes.
4. Mix.
5. Cover the baking sheet. Spoon the mass with small balls of lumps.
6. Put cookies in the oven preheated to 180 degrees and bake for one minute. Disconnect.
7. Do not open the door. As the oven cools completely, you can take out cookies and pour tea.

## 46. COOKIES "MAZURKA" WITH WALNUTS AND RAISINS

**INGREDIENTS**

- Raisins - 1 cup
- Walnuts - 1 cup
- Chicken eggs - 2 pcs.
- Wheat flour - 1 cup
- Sugar - 1 cup
- Dough baking powder - 1.5 tsp.
- Butter - 10 g to lubricate the mold

**PREPARATION**

1. Let's start making cookies by separating the whites from the yolks.
2. In a bowl, beat sugar with proteins with a mixer until stable peaks.
3. Add the yolk to the sugar-protein mass. Mix everything with a mixer.
4. Add the baking powder to the bowl.
5. At the very end, add the flour and knead the dough.
6. If your raisins are too dry, you can pre-soak it in hot water for 15-20 minutes and then drain the water. Add raisins to the dough.
7. Grind walnuts in a mortar.
8. Add the nuts to the bowl to the rest of the dough ingredients. Mix again all the ingredients of the dough
9. A baking dish or a baking sheet with a sheet of parchment paper (grease it with butter) or a silicone mat, spread the dough in a thin layer, up to 1 cm thick, over the sheet and send it to a preheated to 190-200 degrees C for 15 minutes.
10. This is what the Mazurka cookies look like with walnuts and raisins after baking
11. Hot cut the cookies into rhombuses or squares of any size.
12. Let the Mazurka cookies cool and serve.

## INGREDIENTS

- Eggplant - 2 pcs.
- Walnuts - 80 g
- Parsley - 20 g
- Cilantro - 20 g
- Onions - 60 g
- Garlic - 2 cloves
- Suneli hops - 5 g
- Salt to taste
- Wine vinegar - 1 tbsp.
- Vegetable oil for frying - 3 tbsp.

## PREPARATION

1. Peel and slice the eggplant in longitudinal slices. Salt on all sides and let lie for about 5 minutes, then rinse with salt and squeeze well.
2. Fry the eggplant plates in a well-heated oil pan. Put on a paper towel so that excess oil is absorbed into the towel.
3. Crush the nuts, Do it with a coffee grinder; try not to turn into flour.
4. Finely chop the onion, add chopped herbs.
5. Add garlic crushed garlic into the mixture.

6. Stir the resulting mixture. Add vinegar (I haven't found any wine, I've taken a balsamic one, and the aroma will be different) and hops-suneli. If too cool, pour in water so that the mass can be slightly smeared.
7. It remains to stuff the plates of eggplant. On one half of the fried strip, spread the nut-spicy filling.
8. We cover with the second half. So do with all the plates of eggplant.
9. We spread the eggplants in Abkhazian style on a dish, let it brew for a few hours, and serve as a snack, garnished with onion rings, herbs, pomegranate seeds.

## INGREDIENTS

- Puff pastry - 500 g
- Apples - 700 g
- Walnut - 100 g
- Raisins - 50 g (optional)
- Butter - 40 g
- Cinnamon - 0.5-1 tsp (taste)
- Sugar - 70-100 g (to taste)
- Wheat flour - for working with dough
- Chicken Egg - 1 pc. (optional)
- Powdered sugar - 1 tbsp. (optional)

## PREPARATION

1. Peel off the apples, take out the core and cut into four parts. We cut each part into thin slices.
2. Melt a piece of butter in a frying pan, add chopped apples and, stirring occasionally, simmer the apples for 5-7 minutes without covering.
3. Add sugar and ground cinnamon to the apples. Stir, put out still 3 minutes. The amount of sugar should be regulated depending on the sweetness of apples, to your liking. Add 50 grams of sugar

immediately, and when the sugar has melted, try the filling and add more if necessary.

4. Turning off the fire, completely cool the filling before proceeding with further cooking. While the filling is cooling, we will also unfreeze the puff pastry, leaving it at room temperature for 30-40 minutes.

5. Pour raisins with hot water and leave for 5-10 minutes, so that it swells a little.

6. Grind the walnuts with a knife, in a blender or coffee grinder to the state of small crumbs.

7. We lay out the puff pastry on a surface sprinkled with flour and divide into two parts. We remove one part in the refrigerator, and in the meantime we roll out the second to a thickness of about 2-3 mm.

8. Sprinkle the dough with half the crumbs, so that 2-3 cm of clean dough is left along its vertical edges and near horizontal, and about 7-8 cm along the far edge of the dough.

9. Put the chilled apple filling on the nut crumbs.

10. With raisins, salt the water as much as possible (you can squeeze it slightly to remove excess liquid). Separating half the raisins, distribute it on the surface of the apple filling.

11. Roll the dough with the filling into the roll, tucking the edges and gently pinching the seam. If the

kitchen is hot also the dough has softened by this time - place the roll in the refrigerator for 15 minutes before starting to bake.

12. On a baking sheet lined with baking paper, lay the roll seam down. On the top surface of the roll we make cuts every 2-3 cm (cut the top layer of dough to the filling). Lubricate the surface of the roll with a beaten egg.

13. Place the roll in the oven preheated to 180 degrees and bake for 30-35 minutes until golden brown. In the meantime, repeat the whole process with the remaining half of the dough and filling.

14. Puff pastry roll with apples is ready. Cut it into portions, sprinkle with powdered sugar and serve

## 49. STRING BEAN SALAD WITH WALNUTS

**INGREDIENTS**

- Green beans - 400 g
- Walnut - 3 tablespoons
- Parsley - 0.5 bunch
- Salad onion - 0.5-1 pcs.
- Olive oil - 4 tsp
- Dijon mustard - 1-2 tsp (taste)

- Wine Red / Balsamic Vinegar - 2 tsp
- Honey - 1-2 tsp (taste)
- Salt to taste
- Ground black pepper to taste

## PREPARATION

1. Fry the nuts inside a dry frying pan for several minutes until a nutty flavor appears.
2. Steam the string beans to the desired degree of readiness. For frozen thin green beans, as a rule, 5-8 minutes of cooking over medium heat is enough. Beans should remain resilient, slightly crispy, but delicate in taste.
3. Prepare a salad dressing by mixing olive oil, vinegar, honey and mustard.
4. Cut the red onion into quarters or thin half rings, chop the toasted nuts coarsely, and chop the parsley.
5. Place the steamed beans in a salad bowl. Add onions, nuts and parsley.
   To preserve a bright green color, beans can be pre-doused with cold water, but this should be done quickly so that inside the bean pods remain warm.
6. Add dressing to prepared salad ingredients and mix everything carefully.
7. Add salt and then ground black pepper to taste.

8. Bean salad with walnuts is ready. Serve the salad warm up or at room temperature

# 50. BANANA CRUMBLE

## INGREDIENTS

- Butter - 50 g
- Sugar - 2 tbsp.
- Wheat flour - 3 tbsp. (with a slide)
- Walnut Kernels - 30 g
- Banana - 2 pcs.

## PREPARATION

1. Combine cold butter with sugar and flour.
2. Stir with a quick motion with a fork (or rub with your hands) until crumbs form.
3. Chop walnuts with a knife into medium pieces and add to the sand mass. Mix
4. Peel and slice the bananas into small pieces.
5. Put the bananas in a suitable shape. For the preparation of crumble, you can take portioned molds or one large one.
6. On top of the bananas, evenly distribute all the chips.
7. Send the dessert form to the oven preheated to 180 degrees. Bake for 20-25 minutes, until golden brown.
8. Delicious banana crumble can be served.

# 51. BROWNIES WITH MILK AND DARK CHOCOLATE

## INGREDIENTS

- Milk chocolate - 100 g
- Dark chocolate - 100 g
- Wheat flour - 1.25 cups
- Butter - 225 g
- Chicken egg - 4 pieces
- Sugar - 2 cups
- Vanillin – taste
- Salt - 1 teaspoon
- Nuts – taste

## PREPARATION

1. Break the chocolate to pieces and melt in a water bath with butter so that there are no lumps left.
2. Add a glass of sugar and mix for 30 seconds. Add vanillin. Remove from heat and allow cooling.
3. Beat two eggs with 0.5 cups of sugar until completely dissolved. Gently pour into the chocolate mixture, stirring constantly. If the chocolate mixture is hot, the eggs can be cooked.

4. Beat the remaining 2 eggs with sugar at full capacity for 5 minutes - the mass should increase in volume by 2 times. Stir in the chocolate mass.
5. Sift flour with salt. Stir in the mixture (I whisk lightly with a mixer). Nuts can be added as desired.
6. Preheat the oven to 180 degrees. Cover the baking dish (about 20x20 cm) with parchment paper and grease with butter or vegetable oil (do not cover paper with disposable forms). It can also be made in the form of cupcakes.
7. Pour the dough (by consistency, it should turn out as a thick sour cream). Level the top and put in the oven on the middle shelf.
8. The baking time depends on the oven for about 25-50 minutes. Readiness is checked with a stick or a knife - if there is liquid chocolate on the tip, and then sends it back to the oven, if there is slightly wet dough, and then the brownie is ready. If baked in the form of cupcakes, then the baking time will be reduced depending on their size. Large, bake for 35 minutes. Serve with various creams or syrups.

## 52. BROWNIE WITH BANANA AND DARK CHOCOLATE

**INGREDIENTS**

- Butter - 100 g
- Dark chocolate - 100 g
- Wheat flour - 70 g
- Bananas - 1 piece
- Chicken egg - 2 pieces
- Sugar - 2 tablespoons
- Baking powder - 1 teaspoon

**PREPARATION**

1. Melt butter and chocolate over low heat. Remove and cool.

2. Beat eggs and sugar with a whisk.

3. Pour chocolate into the sugar mixture. Mix.

4. Pour flour and baking powder. Stir again.

5. Pour the mixture into a baking dish. Cut the banana into thin slices and drown in chocolate.

6. Bake for 30–35 minutes at a temperature of 180 degrees.

7. Cool. Cut into slices, garnish with icing sugar.

# 53. VANILLA BROWNIE WITH WALNUTS AND DARK CHOCOLATE

## INGREDIENTS

- Dark chocolate - 200 g
- Butter - 150 g
- Vanilla extract - 1 teaspoon
- Chicken egg - 4 pieces
- Wheat flour - 100 g
- Cocoa powder - 1.5 tablespoons
- Peeled walnuts - 100 g
- Sugar - ½ cup

## PREPARATION

1. Preheat the oven to 180 degrees.

2. Cut the chocolate and butter into pieces and melt together in a water bath. Let cool.

3. Pour sugar into melted chocolate. Add vanilla and eggs, mixing after each.

4. Sift the flour and cocoa; add it to the same mixture.

5. Add nuts here. Pour into the form and bake for 20-25 minutes.

## INGREDIENTS

- Baking powder - 2 teaspoons
- Dark chocolate - 400 g
- Butter - 400 g
- Sugar - 500 g
- Chicken egg - 6 items
- Wheat flour - 250 g
- Walnuts - 300 g

## PREPARATION

1. Break the chocolate (300 grams) into pieces, put in a bowl and place in a water bath. Add the diced butter to the chocolate. Melt chocolate with butter until smooth, stirring.
2. Add sugar, mix well and remove the pan from the water bath. If the sugar mixture is quite hot, you need to cool it a bit before introducing the eggs so that the eggs do not curl. Insert eggs one at a time, stirring each time until smooth.
3. Sift flour with baking powder. Pour flour with baking powder into the chocolate-egg mixture and mix.

4. Chop the chocolate (100 grams) and nuts, add to the dough and mix.
5. Lubricate the baking dish with oil, cover with parchment and grease again with a thin layer of oil. Put the dough in the form and flatten.
6. Bake the brownies in an oven heated to 170 degrees for about 35–40 minutes, or until the toothpick comes out dry. The main thing is not to dry the brownie. The cake should remain a little wet. Remove the cake out from the oven and cool, or even better, put it in the refrigerator for 8-12 hours (or overnight).
7. Cut the brownies into square cakes and serve with tea.

# 55. HOT CHOCOLATE WITH VANILLA AND DARK CHOCOLATE

## INGREDIENTS

- Sugar - 4 cups
- Vanilla pod - ½ pieces
- Dark chocolate - 680 g
- Milk chocolate - 230 g
- Cocoa powder - 2 cups
- Milk - 280 ml

## PREPARATION

1. Pour sugar into a saucepan and add the vanilla bean, broken in half. Remove the seeds, mash them slightly with your hands and add there. Stir, cover with foil and then leave overnight at room temperature.
2. In a combine, grind both chocolates into crumbs.
3. Remove the vanilla pod from the sugar. Add chocolate and cocoa powder to the sugar. Mix well.
4. For 1 serving, heat 280 ml of milk and add 0.25 cups of the mixture. Mix well. Serve warm, garnished with unsweetened whipped cream.

## INGREDIENTS

- Salt – taste
- Wheat flour - 800 g
- Dry yeast - 7 g
- Sugar - 110 g
- Butter - 105 g
- Milk - 175 ml
- Cottage cheese - 225 g
- Dark chocolate - 125 g
- Chicken egg - 3 pieces

## PREPARATION

1. Stir the yeast with salt, 150 grams of flour and 100 grams of sugar. Heat milk with 75 grams of butter and 60 ml of water. Beat the cream and milk mixture and combine with the yeast. Mix. Beat 2 eggs and add the remaining flour in portions.
2. Knead the ball from the dough and leave for 1 hour in a warm place.
3. Separate the yolk from the protein. Cool the protein, and beat the yolk with cottage cheese and grated chocolate.
4. Heat the oven to 170 degrees.

5. Knead the dough on a powdery surface and leave for 15 minutes.
6. Transfer the dough to a greased baking sheet and roll into a layer. Put the curd and chocolate filling in the center, roll the edges slightly. Leave on for 30 minutes.
7. Beat the protein with water and grease the cake. Bake for about 50 minutes. If the cake starts to burn, cover with foil.

## 57. DARK CHOCOLATE BROWNIE IN A PAN

**INGREDIENTS**

- Butter - 200 g
- Dark chocolate - 100 g
- Milk chocolate - 100 g
- Chicken egg - 4 pieces
- Sugar - 140 g
- Wheat flour - 150 g

**PREPARATION**

1. Preheat the oven to 180 degrees.

2. In a water bath, melt the butter and two packets of chocolate.

3. Mix eggs with sugar.

4. Add a mixture of chocolate and butter; pour flour into the same place.

5. Grease a frying pan with butter, sprinkle with flour.

6. Pour in the mass.

7. Bake for 30 minutes.

## 58. SEMOLINA PORRIDGE WITH WHITE AND DARK CHOCOLATE AND DRIED CHERRY

**INGREDIENTS**

- Milk - 280 ml
- Semolina - 80 g
- White chocolate - 50 g
- Dark chocolate - 30 g
- Almond flakes - 10 g
- Dried cherry - 30 g

**PREPARATION**

1. Pour milk into a small saucepan. Break the white chocolate and throw into milk. Put the stew pan on medium heat and bring the milk to a boil. When it boils,

vigorously whisk the melted chocolate and milk into a homogeneous liquid with a whisk (from this step onwards, continue to cook the porridge with constant stirring). In a thin stream enter semolina, reduce heat slightly and cook for about 5–6 minutes until thick. Remove the stew pan from the heat, mix the dried cherry and almond flakes into the porridge and immediately pour it onto a warm plate.

2. Break the dark chocolate with your hands, put everything in a heat-resistant plate and put in the microwave for half a minute – minute, periodically opening the door and stirring. Carefully remove the plate, scoop the melted chocolate with a tablespoon and decorate the white surface of the porridge with chocolate bar. Or don't bother and take high-quality dark chocolate chips, pour over the porridge and serve immediately.

## 59. STRAWBERRY IN DARK CHOCOLATE WITH WHITE PATTERNS

**Energy Value Per Portion**

- Calorie Content: 735 Kcal
- Squirrels: 7.3 Gram

- Fats: 47.5 Gram
- Carbohydrates: 68,4 Gram

## Ingredients

- Dark chocolate - 350 g
- Butter - 1 tablespoon
- Strawberry - 150 g
- White chocolate - 150 g

## PREPARATION

1. Cover the pan with parchment.

2. In a bowl, mix the crushed dark chocolate and butter. Put a water bath and melt, stirring, until smooth.

3. Meanwhile, rinse the strawberries well and dry (it is very important that the berries are dry).

4. Holding the ponytails, dip the berries in chocolate and spread on a baking sheet. Leave to harden.

5. Meanwhile, melt the crushed white chocolate in a water bath. Sprinkle strawberries with white chocolate to make zigzag patterns. Leave to solidify.

## INGREDIENTS

- Dark chocolate - 300 g
- Butter - 200 g
- Wheat flour - 150 g
- Natural coffee - 1 tablespoon
- Chicken egg - 5 items
- Sugar - 230 g
- Vanilla sugar - 1 teaspoon
- Walnuts - 150 g

## PREPARATION

1. In a deep container, break the chocolate finely, divide the butter into pieces and melt together in the microwave at low power, periodically checking and mixing the mixture.

2. While the butter and chocolate are mixed, chop nuts, grind coffee and sift it together with flour.

3. In a mixer, beat eggs with sugar and vanilla into a lightened, increased in volume, fluffy mass.

4. In parts, mix the sugar-egg mixture into the chocolate-butter mixture.

5. Add flour, nuts, mix thoroughly.

6. Put the dough in the mold and put the bake in the oven preheated to 180 degrees for 30 minutes.

7. After baking, remove the brownie from the mold, allow to cool and then cut into square pieces. Before serving, ideally heat in the oven or microwave and add ice cream.

## 61. LAZY PARSLEY AND PARMESAN SALAD

### INGREDIENTS

- 2 cloves of garlic
- 6 tbsp. olive oil
- 1 tbsp. lemon juice
- 4 large bunches of young parsley (leaves only)
- 40-50 g of grated hard seasoned cheese on a fine grater, better than parmesan
- Salt, freshly ground black pepper

### PREPARATION

1. Use a blender to mix peeled and crushed garlic with olive oil until smooth. Add lemon juice, add salt and pepper and mix well.

2. Before serving, mix finely chopped parsley leaves with grated cheese in a bowl and pours the dressing over it.

**NOTE**: Instead of parsley, the basis of such a salad may be different greens. For example, cilantro, tarragon or watercress. The main thing is that the leaves are young and non-rigid. And try to buy cheese that is as similar to parmesan as possible as or in any case not worse than it.

## 62. UNSWEETENED PIE WITH TOMATOES AND PARSLEY

### INGREDIENTS

- mold butter
- yeast-free puff pastry - 250 g
- Medium bunch of parsley - 1 pc.
- 4-6 cherry tomatoes or 1 medium tomato
- Russian cheese - 50 g
- Olive oil - 1 tsp.
- salt, freshly ground black pepper

### PREPARATION

1. Preheat oven to 180 ° C. Lubricate the round ceramic baking dish (diameter 15-18 cm) with butter.

2. Put dough on a flat surface and thaw. At this time, prepare the filling: wash the parsley and tomatoes, dry. Finely chop the leaves of parsley with a knife and put in a small bowl. Cherry cut into quarters, and if a large tomato, then diced. Grate the cheese.

3. Stretch out the dough a little with your hands so that it becomes rectangular. Put the cheese evenly on the dough, then parsley and tomatoes. Sprinkle the filling with olive oil, pepper and add a little bit of salt (the salt will be added by cheese). Roll up: it should turn out quite dense. Press the dough along the edges of the roll so that the filling does not fall out.

4. There are two options for baking a pie. In the first: you bake the whole roll, shifting it into a shape and folding it in the form of a "snail". In the second: roll should be cut into 7-8 pieces (about the same thickness of 3-4 cm). It is better to cut with a wide and sharp knife. Then shift the pieces of roll into the form, laying them out with the cut up. One piece to the center, and the rest to distribute around, like the petals of a flower - so it will be more convenient to eat it.

5. Bake the cake for 20 minutes. Serve warm by putting on a plate a piece of cake with a green salad dressed with olive oil.

## 63. VEGETABLE PIE WITH PARSLEY PESTO

## INGREDIENTS

- 400 g puff pastry
- 150 g peas
- 1 red onion
- 2 carrots
- 1 zucchini
- 3 tbsp. l grated parmesan

For pesto:

- large bunch of parsley
- small bunch of basil
- 3/4 cup olive oil
- 3 tbsp. l pine nuts
- 3 cloves of garlic
- 1/2 tsp 5 pepper mixes
- salt to taste

## PREPARATION

1. Rinse greens for pesto, dry, remove the stems. Grind the leaves with a knife. Crush in a mortar or whisk in a blender a uniform sauce of chopped leaves, nuts, chopped garlic, olive oil, pepper mixture and salt.
2. Cut zucchini and onions into half rings, carrots - in circles. Cut the pea pods in half. Mix vegetables with 2 tbsp. l pesto, cover with a film and leave for 1 hour.
3. Roll out the dough quite thinly (the thickness of the dough should not be more than 3-4 mm). Fold the edges of the dough in 2 turns, trimming the corners. Pound the dough with a fork. Put the remaining sauce first, then the vegetables.
4. Sprinkle with grated Parmesan and bake in the oven at 190 ° C for 20–25 minutes.

## INGREDIENTS

- 1 head of young cabbage
- 2 large onions
- 1 head young garlic
- 1 small bunch of green onions
- 4–5 sprigs of parsley
- 2 chicken breast fillets
- 3 tbsp. l ghee
- Salt
- freshly ground black pepper

## PREPARATION

1. Cut the chicken breast fillet as thinly as possible across the slices, salt and pepper.
2. Peel the onions and garlic. Cut the onion into very thin quarters of the rings, garlic into thin slices. Chop the cabbage finely by removing the stalk. Finely chop green onion and parsley.
3. In a large pan using a thick bottom, heat the melted butter; put the onions and garlic, fry over a low heat, stirring for 10 minutes. Add cabbage and green onions, fry for 2 minutes.

4. Pour in 1.2 liters of cold drinking water, bring to a boil over high heat, and cook under the lid, lowering the heat, 10 min. Salt. Add chicken and parsley, bring to a boil, turn off the heat, and insist under the lid for 10 minutes. Pepper and serve.

## 65. BLACK COD CONFIT WITH PARSLEY SALAD

**INGREDIENTS**

- 4 pieces of black cod fillet without skin, at least 2.5 cm thick, 120 g each
- 3-5 sprigs of parsley
- 2 rosemary shoots
- 1 liter of olive oil
- salt, black pepper to taste

For salad:

- 2 tbsp. l hazelnuts
- 10-12 sprigs of parsley
- 3-4 sprigs of green basil
- 2 tbsp. l olive oil
- 1 tsp lime juice
- 1 tsp. zest of lemon, lime and orange
- salt, black pepper to taste

## PREPARATION

1. Put the black cod fillet in a pan of small diameter and about 7 cm deep. Add sprigs of parsley and rosemary and add cold olive oil. The oil should completely cover the fillet.
2. Heat the oil over very low heat to a temperature of 55 ° C (check the temperature with an electronic or alcohol kitchen thermometer) and cook at this temperature for about 20 minutes. Remove the oil fillet, pat dry with a napkin and season with salt and pepper.
3. For salad, chop parsley and basil leaves, mix with citrus zest, season with lemon juice and olive oil. If necessary, salt and pepper. Mix with coarsely chopped hazelnuts, mix.
Arrange the fillet on heated plates, serve the salad separately.

## 66. SLOW COOKED FISH SOUP WITH PARSLEY, POTATOES AND CORN

## INGREDIENTS

- 500 g cod fillet
- 2 large

- bunches of parsley 1 onion
- 1 bunch of green onion
- 6 tbsp. l olive oil
- 2 cloves of garlic
- 4 potatoes
- 200 g of fresh or canned corn grains
- 100 ml cream with a fat content of 33%
- salt and pepper

## PREPARATION

1. Prepare a slow cooker and ingredients.
2. Wash the parsley, dry and tear off the leaves from the stems. Peel and chop the garlic. Wash the potatoes, peel, cut into cubes. Rinse the fish and cut into portions. Chop onions finely.
3. Turn on the Multi-Cook mode, set the temperature to 160 ° C, warm the olive oil, fry the onions, 5 minutes, then add the garlic and potatoes. 5 minutes to cook
4. Pour 1.5 liters of water, bring to a boil and cook for 10 minutes. Chop the leaves of parsley and green onions and add to the soup along with fish and corn. Season with it salt and pepper, cook for 5 minutes.
5. Pour in the cream and mix.
6. Fish soup is ready.

# 67. CARROT SALAD WITH NUTS AND PARSLEY

## INGREDIENTS

- 4–5 medium carrots
- 20 g of roasted hazelnuts and walnuts
- 1 medium bunch of parsley
- juice and zest of half a lemon
- unrefined olive oil or peanut butter
- 1 tbsp. I mustard seeds
- 0.5 tsp honey
- salt, freshly ground white pepper

## PREPARATION

1. Peel off and grate the carrots on a coarse grater. In parsley, remove the stems. Chop the leaves very finely.
2. Mix lemon juice and zest with mustard, olive or peanut butter, salt, pepper and honey.
3. Chop the nuts - partly finely, partly larger. Mix carrots with parsley and nuts, pour dressing, mix and let stand for 15 minutes.

## INGREDIENTS

For filling:

- salt, black pepper
- Egg - 1 pc.
- bunch of parsley
- milk - 150 ml
- Russian cheese - 50 g
- Green onion feathers - 6 pcs.
- Yolk - 1 pc.

For the test:

- butter - 75 g
- flour - 175 g
- a pinch of salt

## PREPARATION

1. Grind butter with sifted flour and salt. Add 2-3 tbsp. I cold water and knead the dough. Cover with plastic wrap up and then refrigerate for 30 minutes.
2. Grate the cheese. Wash onions and parsley and chop finely. In a bowl, mix the egg, yolk, cheese,

milk, onions and parsley, season with salt and pepper. To stir thoroughly.

3. Roll the dough in thin layer, put it into a mold. Spread the filling, cover with foil and bake in the oven at 200 ° C for 25 minutes. Remove foil and bake till golden brown, 5-7 minutes.

## INGREDIENTS

- parsley - 40 g
- crushed garlic - 4 cloves
- Flour - 450 g + 4 tbsp.
- pea flour - 50 g
- dry yeast - 7 g
- natural yogurt - 150 ml
- Salt - 0.5 tsp.
- Vegetable oil - 1 tbsp.
- Sesame seeds - 3 tbsp.

## PREPARATION

1. Preheat the oven to 200 ° C, put a baking sheet inside so that it preheats. Wash the parsley, drain and chop finely, peel and chop the garlic. Sift flour, pea flour and yeast into a large bowl. Add parsley and garlic. Mix.
2. In a separate bowl, mix yogurt, vegetable oil and 150 ml of salted warm drinking water. The mixture should be at room temperature.
3. Pour the resulting mixture into dry ingredients and knead the dough. Knead on a powdery surface for

2 minutes. Return the dough inside a bowl, cover and leave for 10 minutes. At room temperature.

4.  Hand knead the dough into a large cake, cut it into 4 sectors. Give each part a drop shape.

5.  Stretch each cake 20 cm in length, trying to maintain the shape of the drop. Sprinkle cakes with water and sprinkle with sesame seeds. Put on a hot pan and bake for 7-8 minutes.

## 70. YOUNG POTATOES WITH GARLIC AND PARSLEY

**INGREDIENTS**

- Ground black pepper - to taste
- Parsley – optional
- Water (or broth) - 1 glass
- Salt to taste
- Small onions - 1 pc.
- Seasoning "Provencal herbs" - to taste
- Olive oil - 1-2 tbsp.
- Garlic - 1-2 cloves
- Large potatoes - 500 g

**PREPARATION**

1. Fry onion, garlic and herbs in a pan with a thick bottom, heat the oil, fry finely chopped onions until soft, add chopped parsley and chopped garlic, fry, stirring, for about 1 minute.
2. We clean young potatoes, Wash young potatoes thoroughly, you can lightly peel them.
3. Fry young potatoes with onions, garlic and herbs, Put the potatoes in a pan with onions, garlic and parsley, quickly fry, and pour water so that it covers the potatoes by 1/3. Salt, pepper, and add your favorite spices.
4. We cover up the pan with a lid and simmer young potatoes, Cover and simmer over low or medium heat for about 30 minutes; add water from time to time, if necessary. The potato is ready when it is completely soft.

## INGREDIENTS

- 40 g fresh parsley
- olive oil - 100 ml
- 20 g mint
- 1 slice of white bread
- Capers - 1 tbsp.
- garlic - 1 clove
- White wine vinegar - 1 tbsp.
- salt and pepper to taste

## PREPARATION

1. Wash greens, dry. Peel and chop the garlic. Put greens, capers, garlic in a blender bowl, season with salt and pepper, add vinegar and chopped white bread. Grind to a homogeneous consistency.
2. Continuing to beat, pour inside a thin stream of olive oil.

## 72. TOMATOES STUFFED WITH SALMON AND CAPERS

## INGREDIENTS

- Tomatoes - 2 pieces
- Salmon fillet - 450 g
- Capers - 1.5 tablespoons
- Olive oil - 3 tablespoons
- Parsley - 40 g
- Garlic - 2 cloves
- Breadcrumbs - 2 tablespoons
- Salt – taste
- Ground black pepper – taste

**PREPARATION**

1. Cut the tomatoes across in half and remove seeds and pulp with a sharp-edged spoon. Dry up tomatoes with a paper towel and set aside. (The pulp can be used for something else.)

2. Free the salmon from the skin and bones, cut into small cubes and put in a bowl. Cut capers, garlic, parsley and combine with salmon. Add one tablespoon of breadcrumbs, three tablespoons of olive oil, salt, pepper and mix.

3. Tightly stuff the tomatoes with a mixture of salmon, so that the top is a hill. Sprinkle with the remaining breadcrumbs and then drizzle with olive oil.

4. Put the tomatoes in a greased form and bake in an oven preheated to 200 degrees for about thirty-five minutes - or until they are browned.

## 73. SALAD WITH TUNA AND CAPERS

**INGREDIENTS**

- Green salad - ½ beam
- Canned tuna in its own juice - 120 g
- Cherry tomatoes - 10 pieces
- Pickled capers - 20 g
- Salt – taste
- Balsamic dressing – taste
- Cucumbers - 1 piece

**PREPARATION**

1. Tomatoes and cucumber cut into 4 parts, sectors. Break the salad, split the tuna into small pieces, and add capers, salt, mix.

2. Top with balsamic sauce.

## 74. SALMON TARTARE WITH CAPERS

## INGREDIENTS

- Salmon fillets - 500 g
- Pickled capers - 1 tablespoon
- Shallot - 3 heads
- Chives - 1 bunch
- Freshly ground black pepper – taste
- Soy sauce - 1 tablespoon
- Lemon juice – taste
- Olive oil - 1 tablespoon

## PREPARATION

1. Finely chop the salmon, approximately 0.5 centimeter cubes.

2. Very (!) Finely chop the shallots, chives (a little, it performs here rather a decorative function), capers.

3. Put everything in a bowl, add soy sauce, olive oil, and slightly sprinkle with lemon juice and pepper.

4. Gently mix. We put it in the molds and send it to the refrigerator for thirty minutes.

5. Then spread on plates with salad.

## 75. FLOUNDER WITH CAPER AND LEMON OIL

## INGREDIENTS

- Flounder - 2 pieces
- Wheat flour - 85 g
- Olive oil - 3 tablespoons
- Sea salt – taste
- Ground black pepper – taste
- Butter - 50 g
- Capers - 50 g
- Lemon - ½ pieces
- Parsley - 40 g

## PREPARATION

1. Roll the fish in flour mixed with salt and pepper.

2. Put a large frying pan with non-stick coating on a strong fire, pour out the oil and wait until it is heated. Put the fish in oil and shake the pan to make sure that the fish is not stuck. Leave the fish for 4 minutes until a golden crust appears, then turn the fish over and cook for another 4 minutes (without touching).

3. While the fish is cooking, prepare the oil from the capers and lemon. Heat a small skillet with medium heat, add oil and wait until it starts to bubble. After that, stir the oil with a wooden spoon until the foam begins to fall and turn brown. Quickly add capers, lemon juice and

chopped parsley. Stir the mixture constantly. Remove from heat and do not refrigerate.

4. Once the fish is ready, put it on plates and pour hot oil on top with capers and lemon.

## 76. PASTA WITH TUNA AND CAPERS

**INGREDIENTS**

- Paste - 300 g
- Capers - 2 teaspoons
- Tuna - 100 g
- Olive oil – taste
- Bulb onions - 1 head
- Garlic - 2 cloves
- Salt – taste
- Ground black pepper – taste
- Tomatoes juice - 200 g

**PREPARATION**

1. Heat olive oil inside a frying pan, fry finely chopped onion and 2 cloves of garlic until transparent.

2. Add 200 grams of mashed tomatoes; boil for 5 minutes over low heat.

3. Add tuna and capers, simmer over low heat.

4. Cook the pasta.

5. Combine the paste and sauce, add salt and pepper to taste.

## 78. TOMATO SALAD WITH CAPERS

### INGREDIENTS

- Roman tomatoes - 8 pieces
- Capers - 1.5 teaspoons
- Basil leaves - 4 pieces
- Olive oil - 3 teaspoons
- Garlic - 1 clove
- Honey - ¼ teaspoon
- Balsamic vinegar - 3 teaspoons

### PREPARATION

1. Cut the tomatoes into quarters and extract the seeds. Preheat the grill and fry the tomatoes for 1-2 minutes on each side until characteristic stripes are formed and the

tomatoes are soft. Leave to cool at room temperature and transfer to a bowl.

2. Combine capers, basil, butter, minced garlic and honey in a small bowl. Salt. Pour the tomatoes over the dressing and mix well. The salad is served at room temperature with crispy bread and grilled meat.

## 79. NICOISE SALAD WITH FRESH TUNA, CAPERS AND ANCHOVIES

**INGREDIENTS**

- New potatoes - 8 pieces
- Olive oil - 130 ml
- Tuna fillet - 400 g
- Green beans - 180 g
- Garlic - 1 clove
- Dijon mustard - 1 teaspoon
- White wine vinegar - 2 tablespoons
- Lettuce leaves - 50 pieces
- Cherry tomatoes - 12 pieces
- Black olives - 90 g
- Capers - 2 tablespoons

- Anchovy fillet - 8 pieces
- Chicken egg - 2 pieces
- Lemon - 1 piece

## PREPARATION

1. Boil the potatoes inside boiling salted water for about 10 minutes until tender. Drain, cut into small pieces and transfer to a bowl.
2. From the beans, cut the tails and cut into small pieces. Boil in boiling salted water for about 3 minutes, drain and rinse under cold water. Transfer to potatoes.
3. Heat olive oil inside a skillet over high heat. Cut the fish into small cubes and then fry in oil for about 3 minutes until golden brown. Transfer to vegetables.
4. Cook the eggs cool. Drain; dip in cold water for a while. Peel and cut into small pieces.
5. Mix chopped garlic, mustard and vinegar, then add the remaining olive oil, constantly stirring vigorously. Salt.
6. Put lettuce leaves on the bottom of the salad bowl. Lay on top the cooked salad, olives, half-sliced tomatoes and capers. Pour dressing and garnish with egg slices and anchovies. Pour lemon juice on top.

## INGREDIENTS

- Tomatoes - 3 pieces
- Capers - 1 tablespoon
- Dill - 1 tablespoon
- Salmon fillets - 500 g
- Olive oil - 1 tablespoon
- Lime juice - 1 tablespoon
- Ciabatta - 1 piece

## PREPARATION

1. Make a cross-shaped incision on top of the tomato. Transfer to a bowl and fill with boiling water. Leave on for 2-3 minutes. Transfer to ice water, dry and remove the skin. Cut into half, remove the seeds with a teaspoon and chop finely. Transfer to a bowl with capers and chopped dill. Mix well.

2. Using a sharp knife carefully cut the fish across the fibers into very thin pieces (the thinner the better). Arrange the fish in 4 plates in 1 layer.

3. Put a small amount of tomato mixture in the center of the plate. Whisk olive oil with lime juice, spices and salt. Sprinkle fish and tomatoes. Sprinkle generously with

freshly ground black pepper on top. Serve immediately with ciabatta.

## 81. PEPPERS STUFFED WITH TUNA AND CAPERS

**INGREDIENTS**

- Canned Tuna in Oil - 1 can
- Bell pepper - 4 pieces
- Chilli - ½ pieces
- Minced parsley - 2 tablespoons
- Pickled capers - 2 teaspoons
- Ground black pepper – taste
- Lemon juice - 3 tablespoons

**PREPARATION**

1. Gently peppers to remove from the stalk and seeds, rinse and place in the microwave for 3-4 minutes (or dip in boiling water for 8-9 minutes). Remove and lower in ice water. Carefully remove the skin without damaging the shape of the cones.

2. Prepare the filling: mix tuna, chili, capers and chopped parsley. Season with ground pepper and lemon juice.

3. Stuff the peppers with fish filling and cool.

## INGREDIENTS

- Beet - 4 pieces
- Potatoes - 3 pieces
- Carrot - 2 pieces
- Salted cucumbers - 5 items
- Green pea - 1 can
- Sauerkraut - 150 g
- Pickled capers - 50 g
- Olive oil - 4 tablespoons
- Sea salt – taste
- Ground black pepper – taste
- Coarse sea salt - 50 g

## PREPARATION

1. Wrap the beets in foil, pour a large sea in a baking sheet, not less than a centimeter, make a cut with a knife in each beet, wrapped, send to the oven for a couple of hours at 180-200 degrees.

2. Boil potatoes, it is important - do not digest. Boil carrots, it is important not to digest. Allow the vegetables to cool. Finely chop the cooked vegetables - the less chopped, the tastier, in my opinion (chopped into cubes).

3. Add canned green peas, I prefer small ones.

4. Finely chop sauerkraut. Peel pickles, chop into small cubes. Add capers.

5. Pour the resulting mass with olive oil, at least 3 tablespoons. Add salt and pepper to taste.

## 83. SALMON AND CAPER TARTARE

## INGREDIENTS

- Salmon fillets - 250 g
- Capers - 1 teaspoon
- Chives - 1 bunch
- Lemon - ½ pieces
- Salt – taste
- Ground black pepper – taste
- Dill – taste

## PREPARATION

1. First, cut the salmon fillet into thin slices, then into small cubes. Chopped capers washed and dried chives. Squeeze juice out of half a lemon.

2. In a bowl, gently mix the fish cubes with onions and lemon juice, add salt and black pepper to taste. Allow to stand for 8-10 minutes.

3. Carefully put the tartare on dessert plates or saucers, garnish with sprigs of dill.

## 84. SPAGHETTI WITH ANCHOVIES, PARSLEY, OLIVES AND CAPERS

**INGREDIENTS**

- Garlic - 2 cloves
- Minced parsley - 1.5 cups
- Bulb onions - 1 head
- Anchovies - 4 pieces
- Olives - ⅓ cup
- Capers - 2 teaspoons
- Ground black pepper - ¼ teaspoon
- Olive oil - ½ cup
- Spaghetti - 450 g
- Salt –taste

**PREPARATION**

1. Thoroughly grind garlic, parsley, onions, anchovies, pitted green olives in a food processor. Add salt (1/2 teaspoon), pepper, half a glass of olive oil and bring the mixture to a homogeneous state.

2. Boil water inside a large saucepan, add salt (2 teaspoons of salt to 8 liters of water) and throw pasta

(spaghetti or linguine) there. Cook for 1 minute or indicated on the packet. Discard the finished pasta in a colander, drain the water and return the pasta to the pan.

3. Add 1 teaspoon of olive oil to pasta and mix. Transfer the pasta into a deep large dish, pour the cooked sauce with anchovies, mix thoroughly again and immediately serve.

## 85. BLUEBERRY PIE

**INGREDIENTS**

- Wheat flour - 1 cup
- Baking powder - 1 teaspoon
- Salt - 0.125 teaspoons
- Butter - 120 g
- Sugar - 1 cup
- Chicken egg - 2 pieces
- Blueberries - 400 g
- Lemon juice - ½ teaspoon
- Powdered sugar - 1 tablespoon

**PREPARATION**

1. Preheat the oven to 180 degrees. Oil a round shape (approximately 23 cm in diameter). Sprinkle with flour and shake off excess.

2. Sift the flour into a bowl, leaving 1 teaspoon, baking powder and salt.

3. In another bowl, beat the softened butter and sugar, leaving 1 teaspoon, until cream. Insert the eggs one at a time and beat again.

4. Whisk, add the oil mixture to the mixture with flour. Mix well and shift into shape.

5. In a bowl, combine blueberries, lemon juice, 1 teaspoon of flour and 1 teaspoon of sugar. Put the berries in an even layer on the dough and bake for about an hour until cooked.

6. Cool in a form and transfer to a dish, berries up. Sprinkle with powder and serve.

## INGREDIENTS

- Chicken egg - 2 pieces
- Brown sugar - 70 g
- Skim cheese - 600 g
- Semolina - 5 tablespoons
- Blueberries - 150 g

## PREPARATION

1. Rub the yolks with a mixer with sugar and vanilla until white.

2. Add the cottage cheese and beat until smooth.

3. Pour semolina and mix blueberries.

4. Beat the whites and introduce into the mass.

5. Put in a greased mold and bake at 180 degrees 30 minutes.

## 87. BLUEBERRY MUFFINS

## INGREDIENTS

- Blueberries - 200 g
- Wheat flour - 300 g
- Butter - 50 g
- Milk - 120 ml
- Chicken egg - 1 piece
- Sugar - 4 tablespoons
- Dry yeast - 15 g
- Salt – pinch

## PREPARATION

1. Heat the milk a little (it should not boil), add sugar and dissolve the yeast in it. Leave it to stand 15 minutes inside a warm place without drafts.

2. Beat the egg and melted butter with a fork (most). Pour the egg mixture into the matching yeast. Mix gently. Knead the dough and leave to approach for an hour and a half.

3. Put the dough on the table, sprinkled with flour, roll into a layer with a thickness of about 10 mm. Grease with melted butter, and sprinkle with the remaining sugar. Spread the blueberries over the entire surface of the dough, and then press the berries in with a rolling pin. Roll them into a roll, and then cut into pieces about 2 cm thick. Turnover, flatten a little by hand and fold on a

greased baking sheet so that they touch each other. Cover with a towel and let it go for about 20 minutes.

4. Bake in a preheated oven to 180 degrees until cooked. Serve warm.

## 88. BLUEBERRY YOGURT BANANA SMOOTHIE

**Energy Value Per Portion**

- Calorie Content: 299 Kcal
- Squirrels: 9,4 Gram
- Fats: 3.8 Gram
- Carbohydrates: 58.4 Gram

**Ingredients**

- Bananas - 1 piece
- Orange juice - ½ cup
- Natural yogurt - ½ cup
- Blueberries - ¼ cup

**PREPARATION**

1. Cut the banana in small pieces and freeze.

2. in a blender, mix banana, yogurt, orange juice and blueberries. Grind until smooth and pour into a tall glass.

## INGREDIENTS

- Wheat flour - 435 g
- Baking powder - 2 teaspoons
- Salt - 1 teaspoon
- Cinnamon - ¾ teaspoon
- Sugar - 180 g
- Butter - 80 g
- Fat milk - 230 ml
- Chicken egg - 3 pieces
- Blueberries - 100 g

## PREPARATION

1. Heat the oven to 180 degrees. Put 18 paper muffin baking tins on two or three muffin baking tins.

2. Sift flour inside a large bowl; add baking powder, salt and cinnamon. Stir and pour sugar. Rub in unsalted butter with a fork until the mixture resembles crumbs.

3. Using a fork, beat milk and egg together in a mug. Gently pour this liquid into the flour mixture, then beat and add blueberries with a spatula with a rubber tip.

4. Fill the paper molds with two-thirds pastry. Bake muffins in the center of the oven for 25 minutes, until

they rise and turn golden brown. Leave them in paper for a few minutes, and then remove the paper and transfer to the grate. Serve either warm or immediately after cooking.

## 90. BLUEBERRY DUMPLINGS

**Energy Value Per Portion**

- Calorie Content: 780 Kcal
- Squirrels: 25.8 Gram
- Fats: 8.3 Gram
- Carbohydrates: 152.5 Gram

**Ingredients**

- Kefir - 1 cup
- Wheat flour - 4 cups
- Chicken egg - 3 pieces
- Blueberries – taste
- Sugar – taste
- Salt – pinch
- Butter – taste
- Soda – pinch

**Preparation**

1. Stir kefir and eggs well, add soda, salt and flour (3-4 cups), knead steep dough. Cover up the dough with a bowl and let stand for about 30 minutes.
2. Cut a piece from the dough, shape it into a sausage with a diameter of about 2 cm, cut the sausage into pieces about 1-1.5 cm thick. Dip each piece into flour on both sides and roll it into a circle.
3. In the middle of each cup put half a teaspoon of blueberries mixed with sugar, carefully pinch the edges.
4. Boil dumplings in slightly salted water for about 10 minutes after boiling. Before serving, you can sprinkle with sugar, sour cream or cream, or pour over melted butter.

**Energy Value Per Portion**

- Calorie Content: 204 Kcal
- Squirrels: 6.5 Gram
- Fats: 3.3 Gram
- Carbohydrates: 38.1 Gram

**Ingredients**

- Blueberries - 250 g
- Kefir - 150 ml
- Cereals - 80 g
- Ground cinnamon – taste
- Bananas - 150 g
- Vanillin – taste

**PREPARATION**

1. Pour oatmeal with kefir.

2. Add banana and blueberries (you can beat everything in a blender).

3. Add vanillin and cinnamon to the cream to taste.

4. Put in glasses, garnish with banana slices and blueberries on top.

## INGREDIENTS

- Cottage cheese - 400 g
- Frozen blueberries - 1 kg
- Buckwheat honey - 3 tablespoons
- Green pistachios - 100 g
- Sugar - 100 g
- Cream 35% - 500 ml
- Gelatin in plates - 4 pieces

## PREPARATION

1. Turn blueberries into mashed potatoes in a blender. Beat cream with sugar and mix with blueberry puree. Soak gelatin in water, squeeze water and mix gelatin with cream and blueberries.

2. Cottage cheese mixed with honey. At the bottom of each of the six molds put a layer of cottage cheese and pour a mixture of cream and blueberries. Refrigerate and hold until mixture thickens. When serving, sprinkle with chopped pistachios.

# 93. CHOCOLATE CAKE WITH BLUEBERRIES AND CHERRIES

## INGREDIENTS

- Cherry - 400 g
- Blueberries - 150 g
- Cherry liquor - 4 tablespoons
- bitter chocolate - 400 g
- Butter - 150 g
- Chicken egg - 4 pieces
- Sugar - 175 g
- Wheat flour - 75 g
- Cream - 500 ml

## PREPARATION

1. Put the cherries and blueberries in a bowl with 3 tablespoons of liquor, cover and let it brew for about 3 hours.
2. Preheat the oven to 180 degrees. Melt 100 grams of chocolate in a water bath. Remove, let cool slightly and add the yolks, the remaining liquor and beat thoroughly.
3. Beat butter with sugar. Combine with the chocolate mixture, and then add the flour.

4. Separately, beat the whites and add to the chocolate dough and mix.
5. Put the dough in a baking dish, padded with parchment and greased with oil. Bake for 25-30 minutes.
6. Melt chocolate and combine with cream. Bring the chocolate mixture to a boil, stirring constantly. Allow to cool.
7. Put the berries on a biscuit, pour over the juice. Spread chocolate cream mixture on top with a spoon and smooth. Garnish with fresh berries.
8. Put the finished cake in the refrigerator for 2 hours.

## 94. BLUEBERRY AND BANANA SMOOTHIE

**Energy Value Per Portion**

- Calorie Content: 202 Kcal
- Squirrels: 4.9 Gram
- Fats: 1.8 Gram
- Carbohydrates: 43.5 Gram

**Ingredients**

- Lime - ½ g

- Frozen blueberries - 300 g
- Oranges - 4 pieces
- Rice Vanilla Milk - 1 cup
- Bananas - 1 piece
- Cereals - 3 tablespoons

## PREPARATION

1. Defrost blueberries on the top shelf of the refrigerator or you can put frozen - then the smoothie will be cold.

2. Squeeze the juice from half lime and 4 oranges; if you like acidic, you can take a whole lime.

3. Peel and chop the banana coarsely.

4. Put blueberries, banana, juice in a blender and add oatmeal and a glass of rice milk (you can replace it with ordinary).

5. Punch everything at high speed.

6. Serve. Garnishing with mint leaves.

## INGREDIENTS

- Garlic - 3 cloves
- Red lentils - 300 g
- Ginger - 50 g
- Turmeric - 2 teaspoons
- Asafoetida - 1 teaspoon
- Salt – taste
- Cream - 100 ml
- Tomatoes - 1 piece
- Carrot - 2 pieces
- Bulb onions - 1 piece

## PREPARATION

1. Soak lentils overnight. For soups and stews it is better to take red Persian lentils or yellow - they are better than others boiled. Soak lentils for this reason: all legumes contain phytic acid, which makes it difficult for heaps of useful substances like calcium to enter our body and complicates metabolism. Soaking removes this problem.
2. Boil the lentils for an hour.
3. While it is cooking: chop the onion, chop the tomato, peeling it off (just hold it under boiling

water for 10 minutes), grate the carrots on a coarse grater and ginger on a fine grater.

4. Fry the vegetables by adding them to the pan with a difference of 5 minutes in this order: onions, carrots, ginger, and tomato.

5. Next, add seasonings. There are two ways to do this. The first one is longer: put butter, squeezed garlic, and turmeric and asafetida on the bottom of a clean pan. Seasonings fried in butter reveal their aromas better. So that they do not burn, pour cream into the butter. And then lentils, from which we pre-drain the water. The second way: if you are too lazy to stain another pan, you can drain the water from the lentils, add cream and add all these seasonings immediately to the lentils.

6. Cook lentils with seasonings for another 20 minutes.

7. Put vegetables in lentils. Boil another 10 minutes.

8. Grind everything turned out in a blender.

9. Serve with pumpkin seeds and toasted bread.

## INGREDIENTS

- Carrot - 500 g
- Grape Seed Oil - 50 ml
- Green basil - ½ beam
- Ground Cumin (Zira) - ½ teaspoon
- Turmeric - 1 teaspoon
- Salt – taste
- Ground black pepper – taste

## PREPARATION

1. 500 grams of carrots, peel and cut across into 1 cm thick bars
2. Fill with water and cook until cooked. We check readiness like a potato with a knife
3. Put the carrots in the harvester, add grape seed oil (it is neutral and will not clog other tastes such as olive) leaves and stalks of basil postponing a few ground cumin and turmeric for decoration
4. Salt and pepper to taste
5. Punch everything until smooth, if necessary adding grape seed oil
6. Sprinkle with fresh basil leaves on top
7. Serve as a side dish

**INGREDIENTS**

Dough:

- Butter - 150 g
- Egg - 2 pcs.
- Sugar - 100 g
- Baking powder - 1 tsp
- Wheat flour - 350 g
- Salt - a pinch

Curd filling:

- Soft curd - 500 g
- Sugar - 100 g
- Vanilla Sugar - 10 g
- Sour cream - 3 tablespoons
- Eggs - 2 pcs.
- Starch - 2-3 tbsp.

Strawberry Mousse:

- Strawberry - 400 g
- Sugar - 120 g
- Starch - 2 tbsp.

## PREPARATION

1. Put soft butter inside a bowl and add sugar and salt, whisk with a whisk.
2. Then add eggs and continue whipping.
3. Sift in parts flour together with baking powder.
4. Knead soft dough. While the filling is to be prepared, the dough must be put in a plastic bag and put in the refrigerator.
5. Put soft cottage cheese, ordinary and vanilla sugar, starch and sour cream in a blender bowl.
6. Beat the whole mass until smooth.
7. Add eggs to the bowl and beat again.
8. For strawberry mousse, wash strawberries, tear tails and put in a saucepan, add sugar.
9. Puree strawberries with a hand blender. Add starch to the strawberry puree and mix thoroughly so that there are no lumps.
10. Put the mass on the fire and cook until thickened. The mass should remain pouring.
11. From the refrigerator, get the dough, roll it to fit the shape (I have 24 cm), and make 4 cm high sides. Pour the curd filling onto the dough. Then gently pour strawberry mousse on top.
12. Preheat oven to 180 degrees and bake the cake for 50-55 minutes. The cake must be completely

cooled in shape, and then put in the refrigerator for several hours or overnight.

13. Curd pie with strawberry mousse is incredibly delicious! Cut it into portions with sharp knife and serve.

## 98. JELLY CANDIES

**INGREDIENTS**

- Frozen Berries - 400-450 g
- Instant gelatin - 40 g
- Sugar - 300 g
- Lemon (juice) - 1 pc.
- Coconut flakes - 3-4 pinches
- Vegetable oil - to lubricate the mold

**PREPARATION**

1. Prepare a container for cooling the jelly mass - line with baking paper, grease with oil and sprinkle with coconut.
2. Sprinkle the frozen berries with sugar and thaw. Make a mixture of strawberries (200 g), raspberries

(200 g) and black currant (1 handful), but one kind of berries is enough.

3. To speed up the process, you can unfreeze the berries in a microwave or install a bowl of berries in a water bath.
   Grind the resulting mixture of berries, juice and sugar to a puree state.
4. Pour the resulting fruit puree into the pan. Add lemon juice and instant gelatin.
5. On a small fire, warm the mixture for several minutes, stirring constantly, until the gelatin and sugar dissolve. If necessary, you can bring the mixture to a boil and turn off the fire immediately.
6. When the gelatin dissolves, turn off the heat and cool the mixture to a temperature of 36-37 degrees. To ensure the mixture has cooled sufficiently, drop a drop of fruit mass on your hand. If it is not felt on the skin, the temperature is correct.
7. Beat the mixture with a mixer for 8-10 minutes until it brightens and doubles in volume.
8. Pour the mixture inside the prepared container and place in the refrigerator for 3-4 hours for final cooling.
9. When the mixture cools and solidifies completely, remove it from the mold.

10. Pour boiling water over the knife blade, pat it dry with a napkin, and cut the jelly mass into pieces of the desired size. If desired, roll the resulting sweets with powdered sugar. Store sweets in the refrigerator in an airtight container.

## INGREDIENTS

- Butter - 50 g
- Vegetable oil - 50 g
- Milk - 150 ml.
- Sugar - 170 g
- Vanilla Sugar - 1 sachet
- Flour - 250 g
- Dough baking powder - half a bag
- Egg - 2 pcs.
- Strawberries - 500 g
- Coconut flakes - 4 tbsp.
- Powdered sugar - 3 tbsp.

## PREPARATION

1. Beat eggs with sugar until white.
2. 300 grams of strawberries cut into halves and fall asleep 2 tbsp. Coconut
3. In beaten eggs, add melted butter and vegetable oil, as well as milk. Stir. Next, add the flour and baking powder. Mix everything well again and pour into a mold with a diameter of 26 centimeters, greased with oil.

4. Now spread our strawberries on top. And sprinkle with coconut on top
5. Put in the oven for 45 minutes, bake at 180 degrees.
6. Ready, cooled cake on top decorates with the remaining strawberries, cut in half. Pour it with icing sugar mixed with a spoonful of water. You can just sprinkle with powdered sugar; it is at your discretion.

## 100. STRAWBERRY CAKE "CLOUD"

**INGREDIENTS**

- Cookies - 150 g
- Coconut Chips - 0.5 cups
- Butter - 100 g
- Ground cinnamon - 0.5-1 tsp
- Egg white - 2 pcs.
- Sugar - 1 cup or slightly less (to taste)
- Strawberry - 250 g
- Lemon juice - 1 tbsp.
- Vanilla or vanilla sugar to taste

Additionally:

- Cardamom - 4-6 boxes

## PREPARATION

1. Grind cookies with a blender or rolling pin.
2. Combine chopped cookies and coconut. Add cinnamon, melted butter and mix well.
3. Cover the bottom of the detachable shape with parchment paper.
4. Put the cookie mixture into the mold. Flatten by pressing with a spoon or fingers. The base should not be thick; otherwise, when it hardens in the freezer, to cut it, you will have to try. It is enough that it only covers the bottom of the form with a continuous even thin layer.
5. Place the cake pan in the refrigerator or freezer to cool.
6. Now let's prepare the very "cloud". Take a large bowl - the mixture will greatly increase in volume. Combine egg whites, sugar, strawberries, lemon juice and vanilla. If possible, add some ground cardamom - an incredibly tasty combination.
7. Beat everything first until smooth, and then continue to whisk until the mixture has tripled in volume. Use room temperature proteins to speed up the process.
   Rub a drop of protein mass with your fingertips, sugar grains should not be felt.

8. Put the protein mixture on the cooled cake and smooth.

9. Place in the freezer for 4 hours. While the cake is cooling, in addition to it, you can make quick strawberry sauce.

10. Strawberry Cake "Cloud" is ready! Decorate the finished cake as desired. Store the cake in the freezer. In a sealed container, the cake can be stored for up to 1 month.

11. Cut the cake, after dipping the blade of the knife in hot water for a few seconds. In the freezer, the cake cools and hardens. But it will become airy and tender, like a cloud, after only a few minutes at room temperature.

## 101. Strawberry Curd Cupcakes

**INGREDIENTS**

- Cottage cheese - 250 g
- Butter - 120 g
- Chicken eggs - 2 pcs.

- Sugar - 200 g
- Soda - 0.5 tsp
- Wheat flour - 250 g
- Strawberry - 150 g

## PREPARATION

1. Hammer eggs in a bowl and add sugar.
2. Beat eggs using sugar using a mixer until smooth and fluffy.
3. Melt the butter inside water bath or microwave, cool and add to the egg mixture. Once again, beat everything with a mixer.
4. Add cottage cheese and mix (cottage cheese of any fat content is suitable for this recipe).
5. Pour the sifted flour with soda and mix again.
6. The dough will turn out quite thick, but at the same time soft and not clogged.
7. Put the dough in muffin tins. If you bake cupcakes in metal molds, grease them with butter, silicone does not need to be lubricated. During baking, the dough rises well, so do not fill the molds to the top.
8. Wash strawberries well, dry and remove the stalks. Put a berry in each tin, squeezing it a little in the dough.
9. Send the cupcakes to the oven preheated to 180 degrees and bake until they are a beautiful golden

color (25-30 minutes). The baking time depends on your oven.

10. Remove the prepared curd muffins with strawberries from the mold and let them cool completely.

## 102. Strawberry Sponge Cake

**INGREDIENTS**

- Vegetable oil - 50 ml.
- Vanillin - 1 g
- Sugar - 5 tbsp.
- Eggs - 3 pcs.
- Food coloring - 0.125 g
- Wheat flour - 1 cup
- Baking powder - 1 tsp.
- Strawberry puree - 80 g
- Salt - 1 pinch

Cream:

- Powdered whipped cream - 1 packet (30 g)
- Milk - 65 ml.
- Cream (20%) - 65 ml.

Strawberry Smoothie:

- Frozen Strawberries - 150 g
- Powdered sugar - 2 tbsp. l

Decoration and impregnation:

- Strawberry puree - 80 g
- Black Chocolate - 100 g
- Butter - 20 g

## PREPARATION

1. Separately, in a bowl, mix all the dry ingredients - flour, half sugar, necessarily salt, several crystals of dry dye, baking powder and vanillin.
2. Large eggs are divided into proteins and yolks. Beat the whites with half the remaining sugar and a pinch of salt. Grind the yolks with a whisk. Punch strawberries in a blender with powdered sugar. You cannot defrost it. Mashed potatoes are divided into two parts.
3. Add half the strawberry puree to the yolks, pour in the vegetable oil and stir well. We use only a hand whisk. Then gradually pour the whole dry mixture with flour. Do not immediately stir all the flour, leave a couple of spoons; otherwise it will turn out too thick. In several stages, mix whipped proteins to the strawberry mass. This is best done with a spatula.

4. It is necessary to try to interfere with proteins only in one direction, so as not to lose air bubbles. Do not rub anything. Put magnificent dough on a baking sheet with parchment. Bake for 12 -13 minutes at 180 degrees.
5. Carefully peel off the finished biscuit from the paper, prying it with a spatula and roll it up with a tight roll using the same parchment.
6. Allow the roll to cool completely when folded.
7. Meanwhile, prepare any cream. I whipped powdered cream-cream from a pack with milk. Unroll the roll and grease the surface with strawberry puree.
8. Then spread with whipped cream. And again tightly wrap in a roll. Let it cool for several hours.
9. To decorate, grease the surface of the roll with melted chocolate with butter or decorate as desired.

## 103. SALAD WITH STRAWBERRIES, MOZZARELLA AND ARUGULA

**INGREDIENTS**

- Fresh strawberries - 300 g
- Arugula - 100 g

- Mozzarella Cheese - 250 g
- Salt to taste
- Balsamic cream to taste
- Olive oil to taste
- Ground black pepper - to taste

**PREPARATION**

1. Wash strawberries, dry with a paper towel and cut in half.
2. Dice the cheese.
3. Place the arugula at the bottom of the salad bowl.
4. Top with mozzarella and strawberries.
5. Salad and pepper to taste. Sprinkle with olive oil and balsamic cream.
6. Salad with strawberries, mozzarella and arugula is ready. Serve chilled.

## 104. STRAWBERRY JAM TART

**INGREDIENTS**

Dough:

- Flour - 350-400 g
- Butter (frozen) - 200 g
- Sugar - 40 g
- Baking powder - 10 g

- Egg (large) - 1 pc.
- Salt - a pinch
- Vanillin - to taste

Filling:

- Strawberry Jam - 400 g

## PREPARATION

1. Pour baking powder into flour, stir.
2. Grate the butter, add to the flour and grind to the state of crumbs.
3. Add sugar, salt, vanillin to the egg and beat with a mixer.
4. Pour the whipped mass into a mixture of flour and oil.
5. Knead the dough. The dough will turn out plastic and not sticky.
6. Weigh the dough and divide it into 3 equal parts. Two-thirds of the test will go to the base, 1/3 of the test - to the decoration. For a pie, you need a mold with a diameter of 20-22 cm. Cover the bottom of the mold using baking paper. Spread 2/3 of the dough on the bottom of the mold, making low sides.
7. Spread thick strawberry jam evenly on the base of the dough.

8. Bend the sides of the dough to the filling. Roll out a layer 0.3-0.5 cm thick from the rest of the dough, cut out the decoration using cookie cutters and place them on the surface of the cake. Bake the cake inside an oven preheated to 180 degrees for about 20-30 minutes, until lightly browned. Chill and cut into slices.

## 105. STRAWBERRY BANANA SMOOTHIE

**INGREDIENTS**

- Strawberries - 400-500 g
- Banana - 2 pcs.
- Milk - 500 ml
- Sugar / honey – optional

PREPARATION

1. Wash the strawberries and remove the stalks.
2. Peel off and cut the bananas into small slices.
3. Put the fruit in the blender bowl. If desired, add 1-2 tbsp. sugar (adjust the level of sugar, depending on the sweetness of the fruit and your own taste preferences).

4. Beat the ingredients for several minutes until a smoothie is smooth. Add milk and whisk still 1-2 minutes at high speed
5. Pour the drink into glasses, decorate according to your mood and serve to the table.

## 106. Creamy Strawberry cup

For one person

Preparation time: 10 mins

Freezing time: 30 mins

To make this delicious ice cream we need:

### Ingredients:

- 500 gr of very ripe raspberries
- 25 cl of cooking cream
- 235 gr of sugar

### Preparation:

All you have to do put all the ingredients in the blender, and we are going to beat it little by little until you achieve the desired texture, and then put it in the freezer in a silicone mold, leave it in at least 30 minutes.

## Nutritional Information

- 20% Total Fat 13g
- 41% Saturated Fat 8.2g.
- Trans Fat 0g
- 18% Cholesterol 53mg
- 4% Sodium 96mg
- 7% Potassium 262mg
- 10% Total Carbohydrates 30g
- 7% Dietary Fiber 1.8g

### 107. Apple Green Ceviche

3 Servings

Preparation time: 10 minutes

Cooking time: 20 minutes

## Ingredients

- 1/4 cup of lemon juice
- 1/3 cup of orange juice
- 2 tablespoons of olive oil
- 1/4 bunch of cilantro
- 2 pieces of green apple without peel, cut into medium cubes
- 1 piece of finely chopped serrano chili
- 1 cup of jicama cut into medium cubes
- 1 piece of avocado cut into cubes
- 1 cup cucumber cut into cubes
- 1/4 bunch of finely chopped basil leaf
- 1/4 cup of finely chopped cilantro
- 1 pinch of salt
- 1 piece of sliced radish
- 1 piece of serrano chili cut into slices
- 1/4 piece of purple onion

## Preparation

1. Add lemon juice, orange juice, olive oil and cilantro to the blender. Blend perfectly well. Reservation.
2. Add to a bowl the apple, serrano pepper, jicama, avocado, cucumber, basil, cilantro, mix with the preparation of the blender and season perfectly well.
3. Serve the ceviche in a deep dish and decorate with the radish the chile serrano and the purple onion. Enjoy

## Nutritional information

- Percentage of daily values based on a 2,000-calorie diet.
- Calories   61.9   kcal 3.1%
- Carbohydrates   14.4   g 4.8%
- Proteins   1.6   g 3.1%
- Lipids   0.3   g 0.4%
- Dietary fiber   5.1   g 10%
- Sugars   6.2   g 6.9%
- Cholesterol   0.0   mg 0.0%

## 108. Soup 'green

Quantity: 1 person

Preparation: 15 minutes

Refrigeration: 15 minutes (optional)

Ingredients:

Water in sufficient quantity to achieve the desired texture

1 green apple with skin

1 slice of fresh peeled ginger

Half lemon or 1 lime without skin, the white part without seeds

Half cucumber with skin

Half bowl of leaves with fresh spinach

1 bunch of basil or fresh cilantro

1 branch of wireless celery, including tender green leaves

Preparation:

1. Wash and chop all the ingredients. Insert them into the glass of blender and crush.

2. Add the water and crush again until you get a homogeneous texture. If necessary, rectify water.

3. Take the soup as a snack at any time of the day to purify the body and keep cravings at bay. To know more: This cold soup is quick to prepare and has great benefits for the body. Perhaps the best-known property of the apple is its intestinal regulatory action. If we eat it raw and with skin, it is useful to treat constipation, since this way we take advantage of its richness in insoluble fiber present in the skin, which stimulates the intestinal activity and helps to keep the intestinal muscles in shape. Also, green apples are one of the largest sources of flavonoids. These antioxidant compounds can stop the action of free radicals on the cells of the body. Eating raw fruits and vegetables is the healthiest option.

Nutritional Information

Calories 330

Fat 12 g 18 %

Cholesterol 90 mg

Sodium 240 mg 10 %

Carbohydrate 20 g 6 %

Fibre 5 g 22 %

Sugars 4 g

Iron 15 %

### 109. Stuffed Zucchini

Preparation: 15 min

45 min cooking

Total: 1 h: 3

Serves: 1-2 People

**Ingredients**

2 small red onions

2 small brown peppers

2 small round zucchini

3 cloves garlic, minced

300 grams of chopped mushrooms

1 chopped carrot

2 teaspoons paprika

2 teaspoons dried marjoram

1 teaspoon dried thyme

300 grams of cooked lentils

120 ml of fried tomato

1 teaspoon salt and more to splash the vegetables

Pepper

## Preparation

Preheat the oven to 200 ° C.

Cut the tops of the vegetables and take out the interiors with a spoon. Chop the interiors of zucchini and onions.

Heat a pan over medium high heat and add the inside of the onions, garlic and a water jet (you can use oil). Once poached, add the mushrooms and fry until golden brown. Add the carrot and the inside of the zucchini. Fry until soft and the liquid has evaporated.

Add the paprika and herbs and fry a few seconds to release the aroma. Add the lentils, fried tomatoes, salt and pepper and cook a few minutes so that the flavors are mixed.

Season the interiors of the empty vegetables and fill with the lentils. Place them on a tray and return their covers. Bake 45 to 60 minutes or until easily punctured with a knife.

Take view from time to time and if the covers start to burn, or remove or cover with silver paper;

Let cool a few minutes before serving.


## Nutritional Value

Amount per Serving

Calories: 245 kcal

% Daily Values*

Total Fat4.24g7%

Saturated Fat1.915g10%

Trans Fat-

Polyunsaturated Fat0.245g

Monounsaturated Fat1.654g

Cholesterol12mg4%

Sodium169mg7%

Total Carbohydrate3.14g1%

Dietary Fiber0.2g1%

Sugars0.4g

Protein4.56g

## 110. Pumpkins with Quinoa

Preparation: 5 mins

Cooking Time: Approx. 20 mins

Number of Serving: 2

**Ingredients**

- ✓ 2 medium violin pumpkins
- ✓ 150 g of tricolor quinoa
- ✓ 200 g cooked chickpeas
- ✓ 30 g of pine nuts
- ✓ 40 g of blueberries
- ✓ Dried reds

- ✓ A few sprigs of parsley
- ✓ 4 tablespoons extra virgin olive oil
- ✓ Salt
- ✓ Pepper
- ✓ 1 teaspoon turmeric
- ✓ 100 g fresh spinach

**Preparation**

Cut the pumpkins in half lengthwise and, with the help of a spoon, remove the seeds. Place them inside baking dish lined with sulfurized paper and cook in the preheated oven at 200 degrees for 1 hour. Click with a knife to check that they are well cooked, remove from the oven and let it temper.

Wash the quinoa. In a saucepan, boil plenty of salt water and add the quinoa. Cook 20 minutes, drain and reserve. With the assistance of a spoon, empty the pumpkins, leaving a little pulp so as not to break the peel.

Heat a pan with olive oil, add the chopped pumpkin pulp, quinoa, cooked and drained chickpeas, pine nuts, cranberries, and chopped parsley. Season with salt, pepper and small turmeric. Sauté a couple of minutes and, finally, add fresh spinach. Saute one more minute and remove from heat. Fill the pumpkins with the mixture, sprinkle with a pinch of turmeric and serve.

**Nutritional Value:**

Calories: 190.

Sugar: 6.4g.

Fat: 6g.

Carbohydrates: 27.3g.

Fiber: 6.8g.

Protein: 7g.

111. Pea salad, gourmet peas, grapefruit
A fresh, crunchy and fruity starter.

6 People

Preparation Time: 20 Min

Cooking Time: 10 Min

Calories: 1 Cal / Pers.

## Ingredients

1 pink grapefruit

800 g shelled peas

200 g gourmet peas

2 fresh onions with the stem

1 tray of sprouted seeds

1 drizzles of olive oil

1 dash of apple cider vinegar

1 tablespoon old-fashioned mustard

Seeds sesame toasted

## PREPARATION

1. Peel the grapefruit and collect the flesh (without the white skin), as well as the juice.

2. Steam peas 3-4 minutes and gourmet peas a little more.

3. Mix the mustard in a salad bowl with the grapefruit juice, olive oil, vinegar, salt and pepper. Add the chopped onions with the stem, the vegetables and the grapefruit flesh. Mix well, sprinkle with sesame and sprinkle with sprouted seeds.

## 112. Indian pea dip

A vegan dip that has it all.

4 People

Preparation Time: 10 Min.

### Ingredients

200 g frozen peas

2 tablespoon (s) of coriander

2 tablespoon (s) of mint

1 chopped green pepper

2 organic limes

2 tablespoon (s) of coconut cream

Salt pepper

### Preparation

1. Cover 200 g of frozen peas with boiling water.

2 In a bowl, mix 2 tsp. coriander and 2 tsp. minced mint, chopped green pepper, zest of 2 organic limes, juice of 1 lime, 2 tsp. coconut cream, salt and pepper.

3 Mash the drained peas; mix them with the rest of the ingredients.

### 113. Millet veggie kale Paupiettes, apple pear chutney

A veggie dish that heats up in the dead of winter.

4 People

Preparation Time: 40 Mins.

Cooking Time: 75 Min.

**Ingredients**

1 large cabbage kale

300 g millet or quinoa

2 onions.2 cloves of garlic

2 multicolored carrots

1 celery stalk

2 sprigs of parsley

1/2 teaspoon curry powder

4 tablespoon (s) of olive oil

1 l hot vegetable or poultry broth

**For the chutney**

2 pears

2 apples.1 onion.

the juice of 1 orange

25 g peeled and grated ginger

3 tablespoon (s) of apple cider vinegar

2 tablespoons (s) soup sugar cane

**Preparation**

1. Blanch the 12 largest cabbage leaves for 10 minutes in a casserole dish of salted boiling water. Drain them; pass them under cold water, then remove the central rib if it is thick.

2. Rinse the millet or quinoa, and then cook it for 8 minutes in boiling salted water. Drain it. Chop the parsley. Peel and chop the onions. Peel, peel and chop the garlic cloves. Peel the carrots and cut them into brunoise. Chop the celery. Heat the olive oil inside a Dutch oven, and brown the onions, garlic, carrots, celery and curry for 15 minutes over low heat. Add salt and pepper. Mix the quinoa or millet and the vegetables.

3. Preheat the oven to 180 ° / th. 6. Stuff the cabbage leaves with the cereal-vegetable mixture and form small packages. Tie them. Store the paupiettes in a baking dish, drizzle with broth and cook for 20 to 30 minutes with small simmers. Lower the temperature if the lids start to color.

4. For the chutney, peel and seed the pears and apples. Cut them into pieces. Peel and chop the onion. Gather all the ingredients inside a saucepan and cook for about 20 minutes. Let cool.

5. Serve the paupiettes with a little cooking broth and the chutney aside.

## 114. Broad beans, peas, gourmet peas and mint

A chef's dish to endlessly use spring products.

4 People

Preparation Time: 30 Min.

Cooking Time: 30 Min

**Ingredients**

1.8 kg peas (800 g shelled)

1.2 kg of beans (375 g shelled)

400 g gourmet peas.10 g sugar

25 cl + 1/2 teaspoon (s) Coffee white balsamic vinegar

50 g pea sprouts

50 g sagebrush

1 onion withers

1 cl olive oil

1 bunch of mint

60 cl milk

## Preparation

1. Shell the peas and beans. Bring 1.5 l of salted water to a boil in a saucepan, add the pea pods and cook for 10 minutes. Remove them with a skimmer. Add the peas to the broth, and then cook for 3 to 4 minutes. Take out the peas with a skimmer and cool them in ice water.

2. Mix 2/3 of the peas with 50 cl of cooking broth to obtain a soup. Reserve 1/3 of the peas and the remaining cooking broth.

3. Place the chopped mint in a saucepan, add the milk, and bring to the boil. Remove from the heat, let steep for 30 minutes, filter and set aside. Dip the gourmet peas 2 to 3 minutes in a saucepan of boiling salted water, then the beans 1 to 2 minutes. Let them cool in ice water. Remove the skin from the beans.

4. Reduce 25 cl of balsamic vinegar until you get a syrupy juice. In the reserved cooking broth, heat the beans, the 1/3 peas and the gourmet peas for 2 to 3 minutes.

5. Heat and froth the mint milk. Heat the pea soup; add a few sprouts of peas and sagebrush, season with olive oil and the rest of the white balsamic vinegar.

6. In a deep plate, pour the pea soup, add the beans, gourmet peas and drained peas. Add the chopped sweet onion, the sugar, the rest of the pea and sagebrush sprouts, the reduced vinegar and the frothed mint milk.

115. Broccoli, Zucchini & Onions Soup: Super Healthy Recipe

Preparation time: 10-15 mins

**Ingredients**

- 150 g broccoli
- ½ courgette
- ½ red onion
- 1 C. tablespoon of coconut oil
- 400 ml of water
- 1 bouillon-cube with herbs

**Preparation:**

1. Cut the red onion and zucchini into small pieces.
2. Then cut the broccoli florets.
3. Heat the coconut oil inside a pan and fry the red onion for about 3 minutes. Then cook the zucchini for 5 minutes.
4. Add the broccoli florets, water, and bouillon cube. Simmer on low heat for 4 minutes.
5. Reduce everything to the blender until you get a creamy soup.
6. This broccoli, zucchini and onion soup can be served immediately or reheated later as you wish. Enjoy your meal!

## 116. Irish coffee

Person 1

**Ingredients**

1.5 cl of cane sugar syrup (or 2 pieces of sugar)

2 cl of fresh cream

4 cl of coffee

3 cl of whiskey (bourbon, whiskey)

## Preparation

Step 1

Make the "Irish Coffee" recipe directly in the glass.

2nd step

Heat the whiskey with the sugar (at low heat so as not to boil the whiskey) in a saucepan stirring. Prepare a black coffee and pour it over the hot and sweet whiskey, stir slightly. Pour everything into the previously rinsed glass with warm water and coat the surface with lightly beaten cream, it's ready! Savor without delay. To make your cream work better, place it in the freezer for 20 minutes before vigorously whipping it.

Despite some rumors of modern times, an Irish coffee is not supposed to have the three separate floors. Other variants can be made with whipped cream instead of fresh cream, liquid cane sugar instead of powdered sugar or replace the traditional whiskey with whiskey or bourbon, but the original recipe is the one explained above.

Step 3

Serve in a glass type "mug."

Step 4

Add any grated chocolate to the cream.

## 117. Caramel coffee

Person 1

## Ingredients

15 cl of milk

3 cl of caramel syrup

1 dash of cinnamon syrup

1 coffee

## Preparation

Step 1

Make the recipe "Coffee Caramel".

2nd step

Make a coffee (espresso). Heat the glass under hot water and pour the caramel syrup into the bottom of the glass. Heat the milk in another container until creamy foam and pour the warm milk gently on the syrup. Pour a few drops of cinnamon syrup and pour the coffee gently over the milk (use a spoon) until you get an extra layer. .

**Step 3**

Serve in a tumbler type glass.

**Step 4**

Sprinkle with cinnamon powder.

## 118. Latte macchiato

Person 1

**Ingredients**

Coffee

20 cl of milk

**Preparation**

Step 1

Make the recipe "Latte macchiato" directly in the glass.

2nd step

Beat the milk (preferably whole) with a whisk in a saucepan over the heat to obtain foam on the surface (or using the steam nozzle of your espresso machine).

Pour warm milk into a heat-resistant glass (thick walls), blocking the foam with a spatula.

Add the milk froth on the hot milk.

Finally, gently pour a tight espresso (sweetened according to taste) on the frothed milk.

Since whole milk has a higher density than espresso, the latter will be placed above the milk. .

Step 3

Serve in a tumbler type glass.

Step 4

To serve, you can fill the milk foam with chocolate flakes, liquid caramel, cocoa powder, cinnamon or other spices.

Note

It should not be confused with caffè macchiato.

## 119. Latte Macchiato Caramel

People 6

**Ingredients**

1 l of milk

20 cl of coffee

10 cl of caramel syrup

**Preparation**

Step 1

Make the recipe "Latte Macchiato Caramel" in the pan.

2nd step

Heat the milk and prepare 20 cl of hot black coffee. Divide the milk into 4 large glasses and froth the milk with an emulsifier, electric whisk or steam nozzle on your coffee maker until you have 2 to 3 cm of milk froth.

Pour about 2cl of caramel syrup into each glass and slowly pour 5cl of coffee.

The coffee will come just below the froth of milk, to form 3 layers: the milk at the bottom, the coffee and the milk froth above.

Step 3

Serve in a cup-type glass.

Step 4

Pour a little caramel syrup over the milk froth.

## 120. Coffee Cream With Caramel Milk Foam

The supreme of pleasure. A creamy cloud of cream of milk and vanilla with toffee flavors.

15 min

### Ingredients

Grand Cru Volluto capsule (to prepare 40 ml of Espresso coffee)

100 ml of milk to prepare milk foam

Teaspoon caramel syrup

25 ml / 5 teaspoons of cream (already prepared or homemade according to the method indicated below)

Ingredients for the preparation of 250 ml of homemade cream:

250 ml semi-skimmed milk

2 egg yolks

50 g of white sugar

Half vanilla pod cut lengthwise

Materials

Espresso Cup (80 Ml)

Recipe Spoon Ritual

## Preparation

Bring the milk to a boiling point along with half a vanilla pod in a casserole dish

Beat the egg yolks inside a bowl with the sugar

Continue beating the yolks and sugar while adding the milk with the half vanilla pod

Then, put the mixture back in the pan and let it thicken over low heat (do not let the mixture boil to prevent it from cutting)

Check the consistency of the cream with a spoon and, as soon as the cream begins to adhere to the spoon, remove the pan from the heat

Keep stirring the mixture to keep it soft and creamy

Take out the vanilla bean, scrape it with a knife to remove the seeds and put it back in the cream

Prepare a Volluto (25 ml) in an Espresso cup or a small Nespresso recipe glass and add 25 ml / five teaspoons of the homemade cream or ready-made cream

Prepare milk foam with the steam nozzle of your Nespresso machine or the Aeroccino milk frother and add the caramel syrup as soon as the foam begins to form

Cover the coffee cream with the caramel flavored milk foam and serve immediately

### 121. Hot And Cold Vanilla Espresso With Caramel Foam And Cookies

An exquisite coffee combo with classic flavors of fresh desserts and a delicious cookie accompaniment.

**Ingredients**

For hot and cold vanilla coffee:

Two capsules of Grand Cru Volluto

A scoop of vanilla ice cream

Three tablespoons of milk foam

Two teaspoons of caramel liquid

For the cookies:

70 g softened butter

70 g of sugar

Teaspoon honey

Egg

100 g flour

a pinch of salt

50 g grated chocolate

For hazelnut caramel:

50 g whole hazelnuts

40 g of sugar

Two tablespoons of water

MATERIALS

Espresso Cup (40 ml)

Oven

Mixer

**Preparation**

For hot and cold vanilla coffee:

Prepare the milk foam, add the liquid caramel and reserve
it

Prepare two coffees in a large cup and pour them into a
cold glass

Add the vanilla ice cream ball immediately and cover it with the milk foam

For cookies:

- Preheat oven to 150 ° C

Heat sugar and water until caramelized, remove from heat and add crushed hazelnuts

Place the hazelnuts on a sheet of vegetable paper and roast them in the oven for 10 min, moving them occasionally

Put the butter, sugar, salt, honey and egg in a large bowl

Beat it all for a few seconds until you get a smooth mixture

Add caramelized hazelnuts and grated chocolate

Raise the oven temperature to 180 ° C

Put small balls of dough on the baking sheet lined with vegetable paper and bake for about 15 min

Let them cool on a rack

### 122. Espresso With Cottage Cheese, Lime And Brazil Nuts

The sweet lime peel of this creamy mousse with nuts is the perfect balance for the aromatic flavors of the Grand Cru Volluto .

20 min

For 6

**Ingredients**

One capsule of Grand Cru Volluto or Volluto Decaffeinato

550 g cottage cheese

100 g of sugar

The juice of a lime

Two egg whites

Three jelly sheets or a teaspoon of agar

80 g of Brazil nuts

MATERIALS

A pan: Six molds


## Preparation

Roast the Brazil nuts in a pan and mash them finely

Book them

Dip the jelly leaves in cold water to soften them

Grate and squeeze the file

Boil 100 ml of water with sugar and lime juice for 5 minutes

Remove from heat and add the drained gelatin and lime zest

Beat the egg whites and mount them until stiff

Pour three quarters of the lime syrup over the egg whites without stopping to beat and then add the cottage cheese to the mixture

Divide the crushed nuts into the six molds and cover them using a cottage cheese mousse

Pour the remaining lime syrup over and put the molds in the refrigerator for 4 hours

Serve it with a Grand Cru Volluto

## 123. Coffee with Malice

**Ingredients**

1 intense espresso coffee sachet

1 splash whiskey

1 splash whole milk or cream

**Preparation**

3 minutes

You can use dolche gusto machine but if you don't have one you can do it with a good quality soluble coffee loaded. All right; Put the coffee sachet in the coffee maker and select the amount of water to pour.

Activate the hot water until it stops. Have whiskey on hand.

Pour a little squirt of whiskey, heat a little cream or milk and add it to coffee.

Ready, you can add sugar or sweetener if it's your taste. I prefer it as it is. With its bitter touch.

## 124. Viennese coffee

Delicious!

**Ingredients**

1 serving

Espresso coffee to your liking.

Whole milk (if you are in full operation bikini... skimmed)

White sugar

Whipped cream

Shavings chocolate

**Preparation**

5 minutes

Take the coffee capsule. You put it in the machine and let it do its job.

You fill the glass of milk, add your normal dose of sugar and stir.

Decorate with a good tuft of cream and chocolate chips.

As you can see, very, very difficult to do. Having just spent the day.

## 125. Coffee mousse

**Ingredients**

6 cups

4 sheets jelly

125 ml espresso coffee

2 tbsps. Baileys

100 gr. sugar

Two egg whites

200 ml 35% mg whipping cream

**Preparation**

We put to hydrate the gelatin.

We prepare a coffee.

We ride the egg whites with the sugar about to snow.

We semi-cream.

Melt the jello in the hot coffee and add the Baileys.

Add the coffee to tablespoons to the whites mounted.

Add the whipped cream.

We pour the mixture into 6 glasses that we can decorate with sprinkled cocoa powder. In my case I prepared a coffee jelly.

Let cool inside the fridge a few hours and go!

## 126. Detoxifying milkshake

Also known as weight loss smoothies or green smoothies to clean the body, detox smoothies are easy to prepare and taste delicious – especially when you find ingredients you especially like.

Detox smoothies are powerful to clean the body tool that you can (and should) use every day.

2 people

Time preparation: 10 minutes

Ingredients for 2 people

1 cup of Celery (one head)

2 glass of Spinach

2 glass of Cucumber

1 unit (s) of Limón

2 unit (s) of Apple

1 pinch of fresh ginger

Preparation

Put the ingredients – Celery, Spinach, Cucumber, Limón, Apple, fresh ginger in the blender and then blend till a homogeneous mixture is obtained.

## Nutritional composition for 100 grs.

| Composition | Amount (gr) | CDR (%) |
|---|---|---|
| Kcalories | 191.21 | 10% |
| Carbohydrates | 29.52 | 9.5% |
| Proteins | 7.32 | 15.3% |

## 127. Green pineapple smoothie

Considering how challenging it is to eat enough vegetables in your diet, drinking the green smoothie makes you believe like you have accomplished a health goal for the day.

1 person

Time preparation: 5 minutes

Ingredients for 1 person

50 grams of Chard

1 unit (s) of Apple

200 grams of Pineapple

1 teaspoon of Flax seeds

Preparation

Add Chard, Apple, Pineapple, Flax seeds all to the glass of the blender with a little water and grind well.

Nutritional composition for 100 grs.

| Composition | Amount (gr) | CDR (%) |
|---|---|---|
| Kcalories | 251.16 | 13.1% |
| Carbohydrates | 46.44 | 14.9% |
| Proteins | 3.51 | 7.3% |

## 128. Chile Campana Smoothie

Ingredients

One medium banana , peeled fresh or frozen

1 can (8 ounces) pineapple, drained

1/2 cup of red bell pepper , cored and diced (about 1 small bell pepper)

2 cups of frozen mixed berries

1 cup of water

**Preparation:**

Combine all ingredients inside a blender or food processor.

Blend thoroughly until lump free.

Serve immediately.

Refrigerate or freeze what is within the next 2 hours.

Notes

For a sweeter smoothie, reserve and add canned pineapple juice. Use less water if you are adding juice.

Use any combination of berries.

## 129. Pumpkin Smoothie in a Glass

### Ingredients

2/3 cup of yogurt vanilla flavored, low fat or one container (6 ounces)

1/4 cup of pumpkin canned

2 teaspoons of brown sugar

1/4 teaspoon of cinnamon

1/8 teaspoon of nutmeg (optional)

### Preparation

Stir all the ingredients together inside a bowl. Serve.

Refrigerate what about within the next 2 hours.

### Notes

Put granola or cereal chips on top for an extra crispy smoothie.

You can freeze canned squash that you can use later on main dishes, soups, chili or cooked food.

## 130. Berry and Beet Smoothie

Ingredients

1 cup of pineapple juice

1 cup of low-fat or fat-free vanilla yogurt

1 cup of fresh or frozen strawberries

1⁄2 cup of fresh or frozen blueberries

1⁄2 cup of beet canned sliced, drained

Preparation

Combine all ingredients in a blender.

Mix until smooth.

Serve immediately.

Refrigerate or freeze what is left over during the next 2 hours.

Notes

For a thicker smoothie, use frozen fruit instead of fresh fruit.

Use plain yogurt and ½ teaspoon of vanilla.

Add a banana.

## 131. Pumpkin Spread Cream

Ingredients

1 can (15 ounces) pumpkin (about 1 ¾ cups cooked pumpkin)

1 cup of low-fat ricotta cheese or plain yogurt or low-fat cream cheese

3/4 cup of sugar

1 1⁄2 teaspoon of cinnamon

1⁄2 teaspoon of nutmeg

Preparation

In a large bowl, combine pumpkin, ricotta or yogurt, sugar, cinnamon and nutmeg. Stir until the mixture is completely smooth.

Refrigerate what about within the next 2 hours.

Notes

Serve with apple wedges, bananas or grapes.

For a softer texture, use a hand blender or food processor to mix the ingredients.

## 132. Chilling raspberry

Ingredients

1 cup of raspberries

two Bananas

1/2 cup of yogurt natural, low fat

1/4 cup of milk 1% or nonfat

1 tsp. of sugar


Preparation

Put all the ingredients in the blender. Blend until lump free.

Divide the mixture between 4 small containers.

Freeze for about 2 hours or so. Enjoy as if it were snow or ice cream!

Freeze or refrigerate what is within the next 2 hours.

Notes

Do not have a blender? Crush the fruits well with a fork.

Make ice popsicles! Serve the mixture with a spoon in small paper cups or molds to make ice lollipops. Add a wooden stick for crafts. Freeze until firm so that the stick does not come out.

## 133. Popeye's Powerful Smoothie

Ingredients

1 cup of orange juice

1/2 cup of pineapple juice

1/2 cup of natural-flavored or vanilla yogurt, "low fat or 1 recipient

One Banana, peeled and sliced

2 cups of spinach leaves fresh

Crushed ice


Preparation

Combine all ingredients in a blender.

Mix well until smooth.

Serve immediately.

Refrigerate what is inside in the next 2 hours.


Notes

For a thicker smoothie, use frozen fruit.

Use any type of juice.

### 134. Smoothie ananas plant infusion

This is a refreshing and delicious drink. Pineapple is a bromeliad that helps drain cellulite and is rich in vitamin c. You can add the infusion of your choice.

Preparation time: 10 minutes

Servings 2 people

<u>Ingredients</u>

1/2 fresh pineapple
250 ml infusion (plant of your choice)
1 hypertonic quinton water
1/2 lemon (juice)

<u>Preparation</u>

1. Peel a fresh pineapple
2. Cut it in half to remove the stick (or heart) more efficiently by turning with a thin knife
3. Take one half of pineapple and cut into pieces to help the blender
4. Once mixed, add the lemon juice
5. Take a brew that has been kept cool (or prepare one in advance and let cool) (the plant is your choice; you can also make tea). Add the infusion to the mousse

6. Blend a blender to mix the two liquids that are superimposed because the pineapple is sparkling is lighter
7. Add hypertonic quinton water that will give this smoothie a little pep
8. Mix and serve in glasses
9. Two very cold beverages are obtained (if the ingredients are taken out of the refrigerator). Otherwise, leave 1 hour in the fridge before serving or add some ice cubes
10. This drink is very delicious with the foam that gives an even more pleasant sensation;

## Nutrition facts

Calories 50      % daily value
Total fat 0.1 g    0%
Saturated fat 0 g    0%
Polyunsaturated fat 0 g
Monounsaturated fat 0 g
Cholesterol 0 mg    0%
Sodium 1 mg    0%
Potassium 109 mg    3%
Total carbohydrate 13 g    4%
Dietary fiber 1.4 g    5%
Sugar 10 g
Protein 0.5 g    1%

### 135. Lemon cream

For this lemon cream we need:

**Ingredients:**

230 gr of sugar

25 cl of water

Two egg whites

One little bit of lemon zest

Lemon juice (1 lemon)

**Preparation:**

In a bit of cactus, we are going to put the water, the sugar, the juice, and the lemon zest.

We mix it well and put it in the blender, where we will add the whites that we have assembled beforehand. We beat until we have a creamy texture.

### 136. Grouper in green sauce

A soft and delicious low-calorie fish easy to prepare and serve in green tomatillo sauce

Yield: 2 servings

## Ingredients

- ➢ 2 grouper fillets
- ➢ Salt and pepper
- ➢ 1 tablespoon of olive oil

For the sauce:

- ➢ 2 tomatillos, without the peel
- ➢ ¼ cup of pumpkin seeds
- ➢ ½ cup of green paprika, without seeds or veins
- ➢ ½ cup of coriander leaves only
- ➢ ½ of a jalapeño, without seeds or veins
- ➢ ½ cup of parsley leaves only
- ➢ ½ teaspoon fresh thyme
- ➢ 3 garlic cloves
- ➢ ¼ cup of fish stock
- ➢ 1 pinch of salt

## Preparation:

1. In a medium saucepan with water at the time, add the tomatillos and boil 1 minute. Stir and place in the blender.

2. In a medium skillet, add the seeds and toast on low, medium heat for 1 to 2 minutes or until golden brown. Remove and place in the blender.
3. Pour the rest of the ingredients. Blend well.
4. Pour out the sauce into the pan and then cook over medium heat for 1 minute.
5. Dry the fish fillets with the paper towel and salt and pepper to taste.
6. In another wide pan, add the olive oil and let it heat over medium-high heat.
7. Place the steaks and let them brown, 3 to 4 minutes on each side. Serve with the sauce.

## 137. Pumpkin and apple soup

Ingredients

- 450 grams (1 lb.) Pumpkin
- 1 granny smith apple cored, and quartered
- One medium onion cut
- Two cloves garlic
- One tablespoon of olive oil
- Salt
- ¼ teaspoon of cayenne more to taste
- 300 ml (1¼ cup) of vegetable stock
- Freshly ground black pepper to add taste


Garnish:
- Pomegranate arils
- Some pumpkin seeds
- Fresh parsley finely chopped

Preparation

1. Preheat the oven about 200 degrees c (or 392 degrees f). Line a large baking sheet with a parchment paper.
2. Cut the pumpkin half lengthways and scoop out seeds.
3. Slice each pumpkin half in half to make quarters and place, cut-side up, on a baking tray, along with the onions.
4. Drizzle with olive oil and then sprinkle some salt.
5. Bake for about 20 minutes, then add the garlic and apple, flip the pumpkin cut side down and then

roast for another for 20 minutes, or until the flesh is soft.

6. Take one spoon to scoop out the flesh of the pumpkin and transfer to a high-speed blender with the apple, onion, garlic (remove the skins), cayenne, and vegetable stock.

7. Blend on high for almost 2 minutes, or until silky smooth.

8. If too thick, add vegetable stock to thin it out and blend over. Taste and adjust the seasonings.

9. Serve, ladle soup into a bowl, and with pomegranate arils, pumpkin seeds, fresh parsley and freshly ground black pepper.

10. Then serve.

11. Refrigerate leftovers inside an airtight container for 4 days,

### 138. Double melon mojito

Use any melon you have on hand. You can also choose to use a rum flavored with melon.

Makes 1 a glass of 10 ounces.

**Ingredients**

- 6 to 10 fresh mint leaves, plus 1 sprig to decorate
- 1 small file, cut in half, plus a slice to decorate
- ¼ cup melon in pieces (use any type, such as cantaloupe, chinese melon or watermelon), plus some small pieces to garnish
- 2 tablespoons of simple stevia syrup or simple sugar syrup
- 1 line (1½ ounces) of white rum or rum flavored with melon
- 1 cup of ice
- ½ cup of soda water

**Preparation**

1. Place the mint leaves in a strong glass.

2. Squeeze the lime halves over the mint. Use a crusher to crush the mint and extract the aromatic oils lightly.

3. Add the melon and lightly squeeze it with the crusher.

4. Pour the syrup and rum into the glass, stirring. Stretch the preparation, if you prefer.

5. Add ice and soda water. Stir

6. Dress the glass with the sprig of mint, the slice of the lime and the small pieces of melon, and let the melon pieces float in the drink.

## 139. Basil and blackberry mojito

This recipe replaces the mint with basil. It is also great if it is made with strawberries.

Makes 1 a glass of 10 ounces.

### Ingredients

- 6 to 10 leaves of fresh basil, plus a sprig to decorate
- 1 small file, cut in half, plus a slice to decorate
- ¼ cup of blackberries, plus a few extras to garnish
- 2 tablespoons of simple stevia syrup or simple sugar syrup
- 1 line (1½ ounces) of white rum
- 1 cup of ice
- ½ cup of soda water

### Preparation

1. Place the mint leaves in a strong glass.

2. Squeeze the lime halves over the mint. Use a crusher to crush the mint lightly and then extract the aromatic oils.

3. Add the blackberries and squash them lightly with the crusher until they release their juice.

4. Pour the syrup and rum into the glass, stirring. Stretch the preparation, if you prefer.

5. Add ice and soda water. Stir

6. Garnish the glass with the sprig of basil, the slice of lime and the extra blackberries, and let the blackberries float in the drink.

## 140. Tart apple and carrots soup

Ingredients

- 800 g carrots
- 2 golden apples
- 1 onion
- 1.5 liters of water
- 1 cubic broth of vegetables preferably
- Ginger
- Salt pepper

Preparation

1. Wash and peel the carrots and apples, cut into small pieces.
2. Cut the onion and sweat it in a pan with oil.
3. Add carrots and apples.
4. In a saucepan, melt the cubed vegetable broth in 1.5 liters of water.
5. Cover the vegetables with the broth.
6. Season and boil for 30 minutes.
7. Mix everything together.

## 141. Black bean and avocado soup

Ingredients

Servings: 10

- ➤ 1 can (540 ml) of black beans, well drained
- ➤ 1 can (398 ml) corn kernels, drained
- ➤ 4 roma tomatoes, seeded and chopped
- ➤ 1 red pepper, diced
- ➤ 1 jalapeno pepper, chopped
- ➤ 1/3 cup chopped fresh cilantro
- ➤ 1/4 cup red onion
- ➤ 1/4 cup fresh lime juice
- ➤ 2 tbsp. Red wine vinegar
- ➤ 1 c. Salt
- ➤ 1/2 c. Pepper
- ➤ 2 lawyers, diced

Preparations

Combine all ingredients except avocados inside a big bowl and mix. Add the avocados and mix gently. Cover with plastic wrap (directly on the salsa) and refrigerate at least 2 hours before serving.

## 142. Cream of pear and arugula

Quantity: 2 Persians

Preparation: 20 minutes

Cooling: 15-20 minutes

**Ingredients:**

Half a liter of water

4 pears blanquillos with leather, at its point of maturation

1 bowl of arugula

2 tablespoons of fresh aromatic herbs

The juice of 1 small lemon

Sea salt or herbal salt

1 pinch of ground black pepper

Extra virgin olive oil

Edible flowers to decorate

**Preparation:**

1. Grind whole the ingredients in the blender jar, except extra virgin olive oil and flowers, until a creamy and homogeneous texture is obtained. If necessary, rectify water, salt, and pepper.

2. Refrigerate until ready to serve and, once in the bowl, decorate with the flowers and a thread of olive oil. If you do not have flowers, you can use chopped almonds, some rocket leaves or sesame seeds.

3. If you do not have a bowl of arugula you can also use other green leaves such as spinach, lamb's lettuce, watercress, mustard greens, etc. with the aromatic herbs, the same: you can make with parsley, dill, chives, basil, cilantro or mint. To know more: The pear is a fruit with satiating effect for its fiber content: it is fantastic for people who want to lose weight and are doing a diet to lose weight. Also, it is a fruit with anti-inflammatory action, helps us maintain a regular intestinal transit and combat constipation, and has a very beneficial effect on our microbiota or intestinal flora. Choose it whenever you can from organic farming.

**Nutritional Information**

Calories 197.1

Total Fat 12.1 g

Saturated Fat    3.2 g

Polyunsaturated Fat    3.5 g

Monounsaturated Fat 4.1 g

Cholesterol      10.0 mg

Sodium    181.2 mg

Potassium      149.7 mg

Total Carbohydrate    21.3 g

Dietary Fiber    3.0 g

Sugars    15.9 g

Protein    3.5 g

## 143. Soup 'green

Quantity: 1 person

Preparation: 15 minutes

Refrigeration: 15 minutes (optional)

**Ingredients:**

Water in sufficient quantity to achieve the desired texture

1 green apple with skin

1 slice of fresh peeled ginger

Half lemon or 1 lime without skin, the white part without seeds

Half cucumber with skin

Half bowl of leaves with fresh spinach

1 bunch of basil or fresh cilantro

1 branch of wireless celery, including tender green leaves

**Preparation:**

1. Wash and chop all the ingredients. Insert them into the glass of blender and crush.

2. Add the water and crush again until you get a homogeneous texture. If necessary, rectify water.

3. Take the soup as a snack at any time of the day to purify the body and keep cravings at bay. To know more: This cold soup is quick to prepare and has great benefits for the body. Perhaps the best-known property of the apple is its intestinal regulatory action. If we eat it raw and with skin, it is useful to treat constipation, since this way we take advantage of its richness in insoluble fiber present in the skin, which stimulates the intestinal activity and helps to keep the intestinal muscles in shape. Also, green apples are one of the largest sources of flavonoids. These antioxidant compounds can stop the action of free radicals on the cells of the body. Eating raw fruits and vegetables is the healthiest option.

**Nutritional Information**

Calories 330

Fat 12 g 18 %

Saturated 1.7 g

+ Trans 0 g 8 %

Cholesterol 90 mg

Sodium 240 mg 10 %

Carbohydrate 20 g 6 %

Fibre 5 g 22 %

Sugars 4 g

Net Carbs 15 g

Protein 38 g

Vitamin A 4 %

Vitamin C 45 %

Calcium 10 %

Iron 15 %

## 144. Greek chicken stew with slow cooker

Prep 25 min

Total 9 hr 40 min

Portions 6

Enhanced flavors of the Aegean Sea, such as cinnamon and lemon zest, turn this slow cooker chicken into a quick-flavored, fast-cooking stew with canned tomatoes and frozen onions.

Ingredients

- 2 t. (500 mL) mini-carrots, cut in half lengthwise if large
- 3 onions, quartered
- 6 chicken legs with bone, without skin
- 1 C. (5 mL) ground cinnamon
- 1/2 c. (2 mL) salt
- 1/2 c. (2 mL) pepper
- 2 garlic cloves, finely chopped
- 1 can (28 oz / 796 mL) diced tomatoes, not drained
- 1/3 t. (75 mL) tomato paste
- 2 tbsp. (10 mL) grated lemon rind
- 1/2 c. (2 mL) dried oregano leaves
- 1/4 t. (50 mL) chopped parsley

## Preparation

1. Spray 4 to the 5-quart crockpot with cooking spray. Place the carrots and onions in the slow cooker. Place the chicken legs on the vegetables. Sprinkle with cinnamon, salt, pepper, and garlic; pour the tomatoes on the whole. Cover and then cook it on low heat for 7 to 9 hours or until vegetables are tender and chicken is easy to peel with a fork.
2. Remove the chicken with a dripping spoon and cover to keep warm. Stir in the tomato paste, lemon zest and oregano in the slow cooker broth. Cover; cook 15 minutes or until everything is thick and hot. In the meantime, discard the bones from the chicken. Return the chicken to the slow cooker, stirring and cutting the larger pieces.
3. To serve, spoon stew within shallow bowls and garnish with parsley.

## Nutritional value

Serving: 6 servings

- calories200
- Fat6
- Saturated fatty acids2  Trans fat0
- Cholesterol45  Sodium580  Total carbohydrates20

- Dietary fiber5  sugars10
- Protein17

## 145. Southwestern Chicken Chili Cooked In Slow Cooker

Prep 20 min

Total 8 hr 20 min

Servings 8

Warm up your winter evenings with this spicy soup that only takes 20 minutes to cook.

Ingredients

- 1 t. (250 mL) onions, chopped
- 1 t. (250 mL) chopped green pepper
- 1 C. 5 mL ground cumin
- 1/2 c. (2 mL) salt
- 1/4 lb. (625 g) boneless skinless chicken thighs, cut into 1 inch (2.5 cm) pieces
- 1 bowl (440 mL) Old El Paso * Picante sauce medium (about 2 t.)

- 1 can (540 mL / 19 fl. Oz.) Of Pinto beans or kidney beans, drained
- 1 can (398 mL / 14 fl. Oz.) Diced tomatoes, drained
- Green onion, sliced, if desired
- 3 cloves of garlic, minced
- 3 c. (45 mL) cornmeal
- 2 tbsp. (25 mL) chili powder
- 3 c. (15 mL) dried oregano leaves

Preparation

1. In a slow cooker with 3 to 4 qt (3 to 4 L) capacity, combine the onions, pepper and garlic.
2. In a large bowl, combine cornmeal, chili powder, oregano, cumin and salt. Stir in the chicken; stir to coat. Add the chicken mixture and all remaining seasonings to the vegetables in the slow cooker. Gently stir Picante sauce, beans and tomatoes.
3. Cover; then cook over low heat for 6 to 8 hours. Sprinkle with green onions

# Sirtfood Snacks

## 146. Sand Cheese And Apple Pie

**INGREDIENTS**

- Cinnamon – pinch
- Cottage cheese - 500 g
- An Apple - 1 kg
- Baking powder - 1 teaspoon
- Margarine - 200 g
- Sugar - 1.5 cups
- Wheat flour - 2 cups
- Sour cream - 100 g
- Chicken egg - 4 pieces

**PREPARATION**

7. For the test, grind 3 yolks (we carefully separate them with proteins) with 0.5 cups of sugar, then grind with softened (not melted) margarine (butter), then introduce the flour, baking powder, knead a rather thick dough with your hands, finally mix in roll sour cream into a bowl, cover and refrigerate for at least half an hour while the filling is being prepared and the oven is preheated

8. Rub the cottage cheese, mix with 1/3 cup sugar and 1 yolk (add the protein from the egg to the remaining three)
9. Peel the apples and seeds, cut into thin slices (until the dough is rolled out, it is better to sprinkle them with lemon juice or diluted citric acid so that they do not darken, but you can cut them already when the cake is ready to be planted in the oven).
10. Roll out the dough thin enough on a rather large baking sheet, making sides along the edges (so that the curd does not drip). We spread evenly the curd filling, beautifully lay the apple slices on it, and sprinkle with cinnamon. We put the oven preheated to 200 degrees for 30-40 minutes.
11. While the cake is baking, beat the whites with the remaining sugar in a thick foam.
12. Take out the slightly baked cake and lay the protein foam over the apples evenly, level it and put it in the hot oven again. When in a few minutes the squirrels grab a light brown crust - the cake is ready!!!

# 147. COTTAGE CHEESE "STRAWBERRIES WITH CREAM"

## INGREDIENTS

- Fat cottage cheese-800 gr.
- Semolina-5 tbsp.
- Eggs - 3-4 pcs.
- Salt-1/2 tsp
- Sugar 1/2 tbsp. (adjust to your liking)
- Vanilla
- Dried fruits (raisins or whatever you like. I have a citrus flavor, candied pamello)

For cream and filling:

- Fresh strawberries_200-300 gr.
- Fat cream (sour cream) -3-4 tablespoons
- Sugar.

## PREPARATION

6. Wipe the cottage cheese through a fine sieve.
7. Blatter the eggs with sugar, salt and vanilla, add the egg mixture to the curd, put the semolina, sliced candied fruit, mix and put into the mold, pre-greased it with vegetable oil and sprinkled with cereal.

8. Cut the strawberries into plates; lay them tightly on the curd dough.
9. Separately, prepare the cream, whip the sour cream or cream with sugar and apply the cream on the strawberries.
10. Bake the manna until cooked, but do not overdo it in the oven.

## 148. WINTER MULLED WINE

### INGREDIENT

- Water - 1.5 cups
- Dry red wine - 1.5 cups
- Cinnamon sticks - 2 pieces
- Clove - 3 pieces
- Grated lemon zest – pinch
- Oranges - 1 piece
- Honey - 6 tablespoons
- Sugar - 2 tablespoons
- Anise (star anise) - 3 pieces
- Ground ginger - on the tip of a knife
- Black tea – taste

### PREPARATION

1. Pour water into a pot and bring to a boil.

2. Throw tea and spices.

3. Pour the wine and toss the sliced orange.

4. Add sugar and honey.

5. Cook for 6 minutes without boiling.

## INGREDIENTS

- Butter - 50 g
- Sugar - 2 tbsp.
- Wheat flour - 3 tbsp. (with a slide)
- Walnut Kernels - 30 g
- Banana - 2 pcs.

## PREPARATION

9. Combine cold butter with sugar and flour.
10. Stir with a quick motion with a fork (or rub with your hands) until crumbs form.
11. Chop walnuts with a knife into medium pieces and add to the sand mass. Mix
12. Peel and slice the bananas into small pieces.
13. Put the bananas in a suitable shape. For the preparation of crumble, you can take portioned molds or one large one.
14. On top of the bananas, evenly distribute all the chips.
15. Send the dessert form to the oven preheated to 180 degrees. Bake for 20-25 minutes, until golden brown.
16. Delicious banana crumble can be served.

# 150. STRAWBERRY CAKE "CLOUD"

## INGREDIENTS

- Cookies - 150 g
- Coconut Chips - 0.5 cups
- Butter - 100 g
- Ground cinnamon - 0.5-1 tsp
- Egg white - 2 pcs.
- Sugar - 1 cup or slightly less (to taste)
- Strawberry - 250 g
- Lemon juice - 1 tbsp.
- Vanilla or vanilla sugar to taste

Additionally:

- Cardamom - 4-6 boxes

## PREPARATION

12. Grind cookies with a blender or rolling pin.
13. Combine chopped cookies and coconut. Add cinnamon, melted butter and mix well.
14. Cover the bottom of the detachable shape with parchment paper.

15. Put the cookie mixture into the mold. Flatten by pressing with a spoon or fingers. The base should not be thick; otherwise, when it hardens in the freezer, to cut it, you will have to try. It is enough that it only covers the bottom of the form with a continuous even thin layer.
16. Place the cake pan in the refrigerator or freezer to cool.
17. Now let's prepare the very "cloud". Take a large bowl - the mixture will greatly increase in volume. Combine egg whites, sugar, strawberries, lemon juice and vanilla. If possible, add some ground cardamom - an incredibly tasty combination.
18. Beat everything first until smooth, and then continue to whisk until the mixture has tripled in volume. Use room temperature proteins to speed up the process.
    Rub a drop of protein mass with your fingertips, sugar grains should not be felt.
19. Put the protein mixture on the cooled cake and smooth.
20. Place in the freezer for 4 hours. While the cake is cooling, in addition to it, you can make quick strawberry sauce.
21. Strawberry Cake "Cloud" is ready! Decorate the finished cake as desired. Store the cake in the

freezer. In a sealed container, the cake can be stored for up to 1 month.

22. Cut the cake, after dipping the blade of the knife in hot water for a few seconds. In the freezer, the cake cools and hardens. But it will become airy and tender, like a cloud, after only a few minutes at room temperature.

There is no doubt that sirtfoods are good for the body. The benefits of almost all of them are confirmed by scientific research. For example, consuming a moderate amount of dark chocolate with a high cocoa content can reduce the risk of heart disease and assist fight inflammation.

Green tea reduces the risk of stroke and diabetes and helps lower blood pressure. Turmeric has anti-inflammatory properties, has a beneficial effect on the body as a whole, and protects against many chronic diseases. At the same time, evidence for the health benefits of increasing sirtuin levels is less obvious. So far, only animal studies and cell cultures have shown interesting results.

For example, it was found that an increase in sirtuin levels leads to an increase in life expectancy in yeast, worms, and mice. Also, during fasting or calorie restriction, sirtuins help the body burn more fat and improve insulin sensitivity.

## Is It Healthy and Sustainable

Sirtfoods are healthy and healthy foods that undoubtedly can have a positive effect on health due to their antioxidant and anti-inflammatory properties. However, eating only a handful of very healthy foods cannot satisfy all the needs of the body. The Sirtfood diet is overly restrictive and does not provide clear, unique health benefits compared to other types of diets.

Also, this diet is prescribed to drink up to three glasses of juice per day. Although this juice can be a good source of vitamins and minerals, it contains almost no healthy fiber needed by the body. In addition, the diet is so limited in calories and food choices that it is highly likely to lead to a deficiency of protein, vitamins, and minerals, especially at the first stage.

Due to its low-calorie content and limited choice of food, this diet can be difficult to follow for all three weeks. Adding here the high costs of buying a juicer, books, and some rare and expensive ingredients, as well as spending time preparing special dishes and juice, the diet becomes completely unfeasible for many people.

### Safety and Side Effects

Although the first stage of the Sirtfood diet contains very few calories and is an inadequate diet, given the short duration of the diet, it is unlikely to be dangerous for an average healthy adult. However, in people with diabetes, calorie restriction, and eating large amounts of juice during the first few days can cause dangerous spikes in blood sugar levels.

Also, because of the low-calorie content and low fiber content in your diet, you are likely to feel severe hunger for all three weeks. During the first phase, you may even encounter side effects such as increased fatigue and irritability.

## Conclusion

Objectively speaking, sirtfood was developed not only and not so much as, in fact, a diet for weight loss, but as an effective antiage program. Moreover, acting in a short time. According to the plan, the express program should increase the "productivity" of the body - its energy reserves, resistance to stress and aging processes. Initially, sirtfood food was recommended for football players and participants in rowing regattas. And later it turned out that he has a bonus that is relevant for a wider public: the ability to lose weight and stop the feeling of hunger.

### Wine, dark chocolate and all-all-all

So, what foods make up the sirtfood diet? Oddly enough, with such a diet you can even have sweets . Specifically, dark chocolate (at least 85%) and red wine, rich in polyphenols.